Permanent People's Tribunal Session on

Chernobyl

ENVIRONMENTAL, HEALTH AND HUMAN RIGHTS IMPLICATIONS,

Vienna, Austria, 12 - 15 April 1996

Peace !

Rosalie Bertell

ipb

Permanent People's Tribunal

Via Dogana Vecchia 5
I - 00100 - Roma, Italy
Tel.: + 39.6.688.01.468
Fax.: + 39.6.68.7777.4

International Medical Commission on Chernobyl (IMCC)

c/o IICPH, 710-264 Queens Quay West,
Toronto, Ontario, M5J 1B5, Canada

Sponsors of the Tribunal :

* * * * *

Transcription of the Minutes :

Solange Fernex and Felicity Hill, Women's International League for Peace and Freedom (WILPF), 1, rue de Varembé, 1211 - Geneva, Switzerland.

Proof-reading : Dr. Rosalie Bertell, Hazel Tamano (Wilpf) and Chris Bross (IPB).

Final Editing : Solange Fernex, International Peace Bureau (IPB).

* * * * *

This book is available from :

Switzerland :
- International Peace Bureau, 41, rue de Zurich, 1201 - Geneva, Tel. : +41 22 731 6429, Fax. : +41 22 738 9419,
E-mail : ipb@gn.apc.org, Web: http://www.itu.ch/ipb/
- PSR./IPPNW, Suisse, Mühlelochstrasse 35, 8008 Zurich E-mail: bottomup @access.ch

Canada :
- IICPH, 710-264 Queens Quay West, Toronto, Ont. M5J 1B5.
E-mail : 103062.1200@compuserve.com

Ireland :
- Chernobyl Children Project, 8 Sydneyville, Bellevue Park, St. Luke's, Cork, Ireland, fax.: +353.21.55.15.44,
Website : http://www.aarvark.ie/ccp/, email : adiroche@indigo.ie

Great Britain:
- Low Level Radiation Campaign, Ammondale, Spa Rd., Llandrindod Wells, Powys LD1 5EY, U.K., Tel. & Fax.: (+44) 01597.824771

USA :
Dr. P. Mische, Global Education Associates (GEA) 475 Riverside Drive Suite 1848, New York, NY 10115, Tel: 212-870-3290, Fax: 212-870-2729

Cover Photo: Anatoly Kletshuk : Little Nastya has been operated with success in Ireland.

Foreword

"The most dangerous isotope to escape from the bleeding mouth of the reactor will never appear on the periodic chemistry scale. It is "Lie 86". A lie as global as the accident itself".

Alla Yaroshinskaya

The Chernobyl disaster represents the first large-scale "experiment in the management of a nuclear crisis, and it has failed miserably. It has had a social impact unparalleled in human history. People's view of nuclear technology has been changed forever. The accident that scientists were so convinced "could never happen" has marred the lives of millions, and caused the devastation of what was formerly known as "the bread-basket of the Soviet Union". The scientists were paralysed into inactivity by their own self-deception. It was as if to admit to the accident was an admission of defeat. The scientific community must now recognise that the human body's response to radionuclide pollution is far more serious than ever imagined by the nuclear industry. We have not developed resistance to natural or man-made radioactivity. Nuclear science has even created new radioactive elements such as Plutonium and Caesium, which had never before existed on the living planet. Significantly when he and fellow scientists witnessed the first ever atomic nuclear test, Robert Oppenheimer realised the destructive nature of the power they had unleashed. Oppenheimer recalls :

"Some of us laughed, some of us cried and some of us fell silent. I was reminded of the words of the Hindu Scriptures: "I am become death, destroyer of worlds".

Those words came back to me on my own day of "nuclear enlightment", when, together with Ali Hewson and the Irish filmcrew of DreamChaser Productions, I travelled deep into the Chernobyl purple zone to document the reality of the world's most radioactive environment. It was as if in 1945 Robert Oppenheimer had had a prophetic vision of the consequences of the world's worst nuclear disaster - the Chernobyl nuclear accident that took place on 26th April 1986 - the day the world changed forever.

1986

The magnitude of the accident has not yet been grasped by the international community. Not only were the predictions of ·the health effects grossly incorrect, but few are seriously looking at the incalculable damage to the victims. This is not a calamity where people are dying in the streets of towns and villages. It is a tragedy where thousands of families and communities are quietly suffering, their lives constantly disrupted by ill health and personal crises. Worse of all, they are fearful about their futures. Their lives have been corrupted by the nuclear cloud that hangs over them every day. We have entered an era of nuclear violence, a global sickness of endless destruction. A tragedy that is a stain on human history.

We need to grasp the global nature of its implications. The constant radioactive degradation of our human habitat has to be addressed : ever since Hiroshima and Nagasaki our civilisation has had to face a steady degradation of our habitat as a result of artificially created radiation that has been released into the atmosphere through nuclear testing and nuclear accidents. The world community must respond, and prevent potential and also existing environmental radiation crises. The accident poses a crisis of science, and the transboundary nature of the consequences must be addressed. If we don't join together and honestly face the disaster, to ensure that it does not occur elsewhere in the world, the whole of humanity will suffer a truly irreparable tragedy. In the words of Einstein :

"*The splitting of the atom has changed everything except our way of thinking, and thus we drift towards unparalleled catastrophe*".

The principle of learning from mistakes cannot be applied to nuclear reactors. The potential for enormous disaster is too great, and both numbs and defies the imagination. Not only is the technology highly dangerous, but we must take human fallibility into account. If we truly love this planet, we will need to change our nuclear addictive habits.

The report from the Permanent People's Tribunal has come like a breath of fresh air amidst the lies and deception that have surrounded the true consequences of the aftermath of Chernobyl. It bears witness to the victims and gives to them a long awaited acknowledgement of their pain and suffering. This timely report will act as a vital tool to help

4

us to break the silence and to finally, tell the truth. A truth we owe to those who have suffered and those who have yet to suffer. This report must be circulated and read by as wide an audience as possible for it has the power to change the minds and hearts of people.

"Today no task is more pressing and noble, not only for a scientist, but also for any sober-minded individual, than to prevent nuclear insanity",

Valery Legasov, head of the former Soviet delegation to the IAEA, speaking in 1986. In 1988, no longer able to cope with his realisation of the consequences of the Chernobyl accident, Valery Legasov commited suicide.

We all live under the shadow of the mushroom cloud as radiation levels affect us all regardless of sex, culture or class. Then let us unite together to resist the nuclear threat and renew our belief in the holiness of the earth and sanctity of all life. In our willingness to protect the earth the reward will be great, for our children will someday inherit the earth in all its mystery and wonder. Let it be so.

Adi Roche
Executive Director
The Chernobyl Children's Project, Ireland

Session of the Tribunal

Vienna, Friday 12 April 1996

<u>The President : François Rigaux :</u>

This is the first time the Tribunal has met in Austria, and I would like to thank Mrs Meissner-Blau, Judge of our Tribunal, who organized the present session.

The Permanent People's Tribunal (PPT) has in a certain way followed the Russell Tribunal. It handles structural problems. Following its sessions in Latin America on human rights, it researches today the roots of the violations of people's rights. This is why we were interested in Chernobyl. We know of the past and present sufferings of the victims of Chernobyl. It is very worrying to note that their sufferings are not acknowledged. Beyond the Chernobyl drama we have to ask ourselves what are the consequences for humanity of the commercial use of atomic power. Therefore we shall examine Chernobyl, then atomic power in general, and finally the structural problems I mentioned earlier.

<u>Judge Meissner-Blau :</u>

It is my pleasure to welcome you all to Vienna. I am confident that we will have a very interesting session, especially with regard to what happened these last days at the Conference of the International Atomic Energy Agency (IAEA) just across the Danube. The organisation of this session relied on a very small voluntary group and I ask you for your full appreciation. We have very little money but a very great energy and involvement. We will work in friendship and solidarity, and if difficulties should arise, I am confident that together we will be able to solve them in the best possible way.

Table of Content : page

I. INTRODUCTION TO TESTIMONIES

Speakers :   Dr. Gianni Tognoni, Secretary General of the
                  Permanent People's Tribunal (PPT),
                  Rome, Italy

                  Dr. Rosalie Bertell, Co-ordinator of the
                  Internal Medical Commission on Chernobyl
                  (IMCC), Toronto, Canada

Dr. Gianni Tognoni :

I want to give you some information about the rules and about the procedural aspects of the Tribunal.

The Permanent People's Tribunal was established back in 1979 when it formally became a permanent institution. According to the standing rules, the Tribunal accepts to hold a session on a specific topic once a request has been received. The key proponent of the request this time is the International Medical Commission on Chernobyl, headed by Dr. Rosalie Bertell, who formally presented the accusation and the request to convene the Tribunal. Once a request is received, the procedure is to send the text of the request to those parties which could be considered to be concerned by the accusation.

This time it was particularly difficult to identify clearly those counterparts, because there was no specificity in the Chernobyl case of who is in fact responsible, directly or indirectly. Looking at the different parties, we sent the request to the International Commission for Radiological Protection (ICRP), the International Atomic Energy Agency (IAEA), the United Nations (UN) concerned Agencies and to the World Health Organisation (WHO). We wrote also to the European Union (EU).

We received an immediate response from the United Nations, submitting the last resolution passed in the UN General Assembly on Chernobyl. We received an answer from the IAEA, saying that they were unable to attend because of their great commitment for their Conference "10 Years after Chernobyl". They invited the Tribunal to take into account the conclusions of their meeting. The UN agencies said they were not able to come because of financial constraints. The World Health Organisation commented positively on the initiative and asked us to submit the conclusions of the Tribunal for due consideration.

The Tribunal, as you see from the program, accepts reports or testimonies, and the procedure does not usually include questions from the public. The questions are addressed by the members of the Tribunal directly to the experts or witnesses. Obviously, the organiser of the accusation, Dr. Rosalie Bertell is always requested or allowed to introduce specific questions in order to facilitate a full exploration of the problem.

We shall try our best with parallel or subsequent translations, because we don't have simultaneous translation to optimise the reciprocal understanding. We must be very strict on time limits, otherwise the great amount of material that is presented would not allow us either to draw the conclusions of our work or to reach a fair assessment.

I would also like to show, or at least to record the connection of this session with the previous sessions of the PPT, to give an idea of the complimentary nature of the work of this Tribunal in terms of some of the competence, and also the possibly specific contributions and the originality of this session. As the Tribunal was established in 1979, 17 years ago, we have heard many cases. The last cases were dealing with the structural mechanisms of oppression as being particularly important.

From the point of view of procedure, I have to underline one coincidence which seen afterwards may possibly not be a coincidence but a very interesting indicator. In April 1991, the PPT was concluding one of its most important and long sessions on Impunity in Latin America. The question of impunity was specifically significant, because it was the first time it was raised after the dictatorships in South America. It was one of the main areas of interest of the PPT in its early phase, and also for the pre-establishment phase of the Tribunal on Latin America. What was emerging then was that, after a period of aggression, the rights of people in Latin America were put at the disposal of dictatorships and military powers. The process of democratisation was in fact establishing democratic, or so called democratic rules in Latin America, as was requested by the people. If you looked at the relationship between the formal democracy and the real democracy, it was clear that substantial conditions for the violation of fundamental rights of people were that the democratic standard rules were different. The session on impunity was underlining a

12

point which had already been underlined in the session on the International Monetary Fund (IMF) : the aggression on private people, starting in the late 80's, wasn't so obvious because the mechanisms were more or less legal. There was no clear violation.

What is more important is that it is difficult to classify the victims of those aggressions. Even more, since there exists no accountability, there is no formal mechanism to get hold of those who could be responsible but are in fact anonymous, impossible to get hold of, and are part of the legal institution. That represents a completely different scenario from the point of view of the affirmation of the rights of people. History pointed clearly at the reasons to condemn the dictatorships of Guatemala or the Philippines or the invasion of Afghanistan. But to set up a case on impunity on the actions of the World Bank and the IMF, seemed to be out of the common rules of the law.

The day after we closed the Impunity Tribunal (and that is the interesting connection), we were opening in Yale the Tribunal on Bhopal, a session on disasters and environmental hazards. I think this is one of the areas where all those mechanisms of impunity, including the lack of accountability, lack of direct responsibility, are very evident. The session on the environmental hazards went from 1991 to 94, having as its nucleus of interest the accident of Bhopal, the other classical or traditional accident, the worst industrial accident before Chernobyl. We held one of the first of four sessions in Yale, and it was interesting to show the continuity between what was going on in the United States, the environmental industrial hazards in the South Pacific, and same during the Bangkok session of the same year in Southeast Asia. In 1992 a third session was held directly in Bhopal, with the participation of thirteen countries of Southeast Asia. The final session was held in London on the 10th anniversary of the Bhopal accident.

In Bhopal and Chernobyl, we find that those accidents are representative of more widespread conditions, so that they cannot be considered as isolated happenings. The specific target of that session was to show that accidents are also indicators of an underlying continuing process. These accidents definitely should be looked at, not so much for details of the specific cases, but in a general perspective, which has a lot to do with our subject today.

We mentioned specifically the priority of giving attention to the nuclear issue in general, as one of the recommendations of the session on Bhopal, printed in the verdict, of which Chernobyl was the most striking case.

Chernobyl on one side, represents clearly an extreme, not only of risk but of damage. On the other side, it represents possibly a case of extreme lack of accountability. For no other case do we lack such availability of data. In the scientific literature, which I am studying as a medical researcher, it is possible to find, for instance, some facts about the accident of Bhopal.

If you search for scientific data on Chernobyl, silence is more dominant than facts. We find here secrecy, the same secrecy rule which was claimed in the name of the national security by Latin American dictatorships. Everything has to be secret, because "somebody" knows what is good for the population and for the national security. These were the reasons found by the Latin American Tribunal on Impunity. National security includes economic measures and this represents in fact the overall justification.

I will close with a last connection of the present session with the work and experience of the Tribunal. Something that has incredibly been denied with Chernobyl is now more or less openly recognised : the Chernobyl accident has produced many victims, and the public, which was most concerned, have in fact been the most affected.

If it is true that traces of the accident were found 500 kilometres from the site of the accident, nobody lives very far from a nuclear plant. That is something that really is important for everybody. But what I'm underlining is the point that we find, once again, that the key indicators, like in the accident of Bhopal, are children. Last year, the Tribunal held a session on children as indicators, dramatic indicators for the effects of those widespread, more or less legal violation of fundamental rights.

Last year's Tribunal on the rights of children and on the violations of the Convention on Children, discussed the children as they are presented in the official reports of the United Nations - they are always presented as indicators of development or of absence of development. They are never considered as victims, only as indicators.

I think it is one of the challenges of this session for the benefit of future generations, to see whether in fact children, and those populations for whom the children are indicators, should no more be considered as mere indictors of development, but as persons entitled with fundamental rights.

Dr. Rosalie Bertell :

We appreciate very much the fact that the Permanent People's Tribunal has agreed to hear this issue, and I would like to begin by remembering a very important person who is not with us today. I would like to mention Petra Kelly. She would have been the first one here. We remember her today, in a very special way.

The problems arising in connection with Chernobyl are rooted very deeply within our society, they are truly systemic in nature and we need to identify the structural mechanisms of repression at work in this case. We need to bring them to the public's attention, because I think they parade as scientific arguments, which they are not in my view. It has fundamentally to do with repression,it's fundamentally political decisions that are causing the difficulties.

Currently, because the participants at the recent meeting of the IAEA were the leading figures of the 1991 assessment of Chernobyl, and were the ones who declared that the problems had been exaggerated, and the sicknesses were not connected with radiation, they have been the focus of criticism.

I believe that the roots of the problem lie much deeper. I believe they preceded what happened at the IAEA, which acts like a police force, irrationally enforcing mechanisms which were already in place. IAEA officials are right now taking most of the criticism and I think they have been very cruel in the way they have enforced the radiation protection regime, but they are not the origin of this regime.

I have worked as a scientist on the health effects of radiation since 1968 and I was personally amazed to discover in the literature that most of the really detailed research was conducted before 1951. Since 1951, the myth that you can't study low level radiation has prevailed.

1951 represents a very significant date : that of the opening of the above ground nuclear weapons test site in

Nevada, the first one to be open on the continent. The fallout from more than 500 nuclear explosions spread through the whole northern hemisphere. At that time there was a concerted effort to declare that low-level radiation wasn't harmful and that there was no way to prove that any effects were connected with them.

If we go back to Hiroshima and Nagasaki, we see that from there on, the researchers looked primarily at the effect of a war scenario. They wanted to know how many people would be killed rapidly and how many would be disabled from fighting. These were the main thoughts of the people who did the research, and these were the main calculations that they made. They were not concerned by miscarriages nor fetal deaths, neonatal deaths, they were not concerned by sick people or children, nor by many of the long-term effects which were not tabulated. They were very selective in their research, and in the damage they admitted. I have tried to highlight this aspect in a paper which is available here to the Court.

I tried to indicate that the number of radiation victims is now conservatively estimated at 32 million people. We are talking about workers, we are talking about the Japanese population, we are talking about the victims of above-ground nuclear weapons testing and various accidents and incidents that have occurred. Chief among them is the Chernobyl accident, which was a huge disaster. We will be hearing more about it.

We will have to question here the definitions given by bureaucrats as to what damage should be considered as "serious". The "seriousness" is a decision made by bureaucrats for a community, it's not what is serious for the individual - the individual point of view is very different.

I would like to go back to 1954, which represents a second very important date. In 1954 they conducted the first, from the military point of view, successful explosion of a hydrogen bomb. The H-bomb gave an unlimited amount of fire power to the atomic explosion. Atomic bomb such as were used in Hiroshima and Nagasaki have a limited fire power. When you get to the hydrogen bomb, its size is unlimited.

It was at that moment, in 1954, that the US in particular and the Western powers and the Soviet Union choose the atomic bomb as the main weapon of their military forces. That date, 1954, saw also the launching of the so-called "peaceful atom" program. This program in turn enabled them to organise all of North-America as a large bomb factory, including uranium mining and milling, with transitions to involve the universities in the teaching of nuclear physics and nuclear engineering and so on. They had to win the co-operation of civilians. It is also in the same period that we find the organisation of the International Commission on Radiological Protection (ICRP).

This organisation was born out of the secrecy of the atomic weapons and national security, therefore secrecy is inbedded in the formation of this organisation. ICRP consists of a main committee which elaborates all the definitions and takes all the decisions. From 1954 to 1991 the members of this committee were 13 men, since then one woman joined[1]. They are self appointed and self perpetuated. They are the ones who make the recommendations for radiation protection standards, which have then to be adopted by every nation. They are the source of the regulations applied by the IAEA, indeed applied in a very cruel way after the Chernobyl accident and elsewhere.

It is very important to look in detail at the documents of the ICRP. I was very taken aback that in their 1990 report, they actually talked about "transient effects of radiation", effects that they didn't consider serious enough to receive compensation or to be recognised. But these are exactly the kinds of problems that people experience which they are trying to present to the world's opinion. The existence of these problems is continually denied by the IAEA.

Meanwhile, the ICRP, who recognised them as "transient effects", has stayed very quiet in the background, because

---

1 In 1990, ICRP was composed of following persons : <u>President</u> : Dr. J. Beninson, Comision Nacional de Energia Atomica, Argentine, <u>Vice-President</u> : Dr. H. Jammet, Directeur du Centre d'Etudes Nucléaires de Fontenay aux Roses, France, <u>Scientific secretary</u> : Dr. H. Smith, UK, <u>Members</u> : Prof. R.J. Berry et M. H.J. Dunster, UK, Prof. W. Jacobi, Germany, Dr. Li Deping, China, Prof. J. Liniecki, Poland, M. C.B. Meinhold, Prof. A.K. Poznanski, Dr. W.K. Sinclair, USA, Prof. P.V. Ramzaev, USSR, Dr. G. Silini, Austria, Dr. E. Tajima, Japan. During 1990, Drs. Tajima, Ramzaev, Poznanski and Berry were replaced by Dr. R.H. Clarke, Prof. A.K. Guskova (the first woman, Russia, specialist of acute radiation syndrome ARS), Prof. F. Mettler (redactor of the IAEA 1991 study on the consequences of Chernobyl on health) and Dr. S. Shigematsu, Japan.

their professional credibility is on the line : they can't honestly say that these effects do not occur and are not related to radiation. The engineers and physicists at the IAEA are the ones who are mandated to talk about health effects. I believe that that's an important part of the problem.

There are several ways in which to use definitions, which Harvard University calls "strategic misrepresentation". There are very clever ways of lying, so that you are not liable in court for telling a lie. One is to define an "accident". I'm not sure of the exact "accident definition" for Chernobyl, but I remember at Three Mile Island, they defined as the "accident" only the first seven days - anything beyond that was called "cleanup". When they talk about the dose people got from the accident, not only do they limit it to the first seven days, but they subtract from it the dose people would have got from a normally operating nuclear power plant, plus the background radiation, plus the fallout from the Chinese nuclear bomb, because all of these things could have happened. For them, the dose received from the accident was only what was left after subtracting all other doses, and this of course only for seven days. That in itself is deceiving.

Another thing that I would like to point out, is the difference, because of the radiation exposure, of the Chernobyl accident with the Bhopal accident. In Bhopal, most of the effects were immediately visible. There was direct damage to the people who were exposed and the damage that occurred was very obvious to the people and to everyone else. However, the damage inflicted by radiation takes place at the cellular level, and it usually takes a while before the person becomes sick. They don't have the immediate connection in their minds between the exposure and the sickness because of the time delay.

Moreover, the same damage takes place in the sperm and the ovum and only shows up in future generations and it is perpetuated. That is an area which I think the nuclear industry has definitely tried to avoid, they have definitely tried to play down the genetic effects and the effects on future generations. As it was explained to me by one person from Chernobyl, it's an accident which starts small and keeps getting bigger as you move away in time. It's the opposite of a dam break or another terrible calamity, which is awful in the beginning but as time goes on, becomes

18

smaller. From a psychological point of view, Chernobyl getting bigger all the time raises a fear in the population because of that aspect, which I think is exceptional because it passes through different generations.

I would like to just quickly point out which radiation health effects are recognised by the IAEA and which ones are not recognised, although they do exist. IAEA recognised three categories, presently four since they have been forced to recognise leukemia. ①

They recognise "radiation-induced fatal cancers", every word is of course vital. They recognise fatal cancers, but they are consequently very reluctant to admit to cancers that are not fatal, or benign tumours, and they certainly limit themselves to "radiation-induced". As a fact, radiation does also enhance cancers that are primarily induced by other factors, so they have put a time limit of ten years on this, and they don't recognise any other cancers as induced by radiation within the first ten years after the disaster (so called latency period). Since they do recognise leukemia, this time limit does not apply to it. Some cancers might well be radiation - promoted but that is not a category that is compensated. So that is the first category. ②

The second one is "severe genetic disease borne in live offspring", and every word is important again - it has to be a "severe" genetic disease, that is, one of the classical, listed, very rare and very devastating diseases. The more common ones like asthma are not recognised. They have to be in "live offspring", which means that if there is a neonatal-natal death or a miscarriage with genetic damage, they are not recognised.

As to teratogenic damages, damages to the baby *in utero*, they are now only accepting "severe mental retardation" and they limit the exposure to the first 8-15 weeks of the pregnancy. "Severe retardation" for the nuclear industry, means that the person is incapable to respond to a greeting, or incapable to feed herself. Those obviously extreme endpoints are the only ones they recognise.

Human exposure to radiation involves a whole range of pain and suffering, other levels of damage will be experienced by people. The testimonies that will be given here will expose the levels of damage that involve many more people and much sufferings, which are not recognised.

I believe we have yet to understand that this denial is structural, and that it is built in. It is often argued that most of the problems in Chernobyl come from the fact that it happened under a Communist regime, and that much can be blamed on the political structures. My belief is that the same secrecy has occurred in the West, and I would just like to comment on the Three Mile Island accident we have had in 1979, in the United States.

There are still 2,000 cases of victims at Three Mile Island, which have not yet been heard in the court. The reason for this delay is that the nuclear industry took it all the way to the Supreme Court to say that as the level of radiation that people were exposed to at Three Mile Island could not cause any health effects, there should not be any court cases. This claim was rejected just about one month ago by the US Supreme Court, and they have now opened the way for the cases from 1979 to at least be heard.

The first 11 cases will be heard in June 1996 in the Federal Court in Harrisburg. The nuclear industry has intervened for a second time, using a law that concerns expert witnesses. They say that expert witnesses in court cannot be heard unless their methodology and findings agree with the peers in the same field, and they have declared themselves the peers in the field of radiation health. As a consequence, in the court proceeding, 10 out of the 11 expert witnesses have been thrown out by the court. Now the victims have to appear before the court in June without their expert witnesses. This represents a structural undermining of the human rights and of legal justice.

What I would put before the Tribunal, is what I call the imminent atomic dangers to all of us, because the atomic industry is now preparing for the next nuclear accident. I think that the inherent dangers of this technology are not just the statistically predictable accidents, but the routine releases of radioactive material that are built in by the industry.

I think that the Tribunal should comment on the extremely limited definition of radiation detriment put forth by the ICRP.

I think that the Tribunal should condemn the absence of any international agency in charge of the protection of workers and the communities at risk because of this industry - there exists no such organisation. ICRP makes trade-offs, taking into account the economic benefits. It does not speak for radiation protection. No ICRP member has ever been a recognised expert in public health or occupational health. More than 50% of them are physicists and they speak in favour of trade-offs, they are basically the users of the industry.

I think that we need a public recognition of the human sufferings that are not being recognised by the IAEA. The revictimisation of the victims by this kind of administration must be condemned. We need to address the conflict of interest in the IAEA, which is currently promoting the expansion of the nuclear industry in the developing world. A pseudo-scientific credibility is being given by the UN to this agency, whose members are considered to be THE experts.

I think that the most important question here is the damage being done to the seed, to the basis of future life on this planet. I recommend the abolition of both ICRP and IAEA as essential to securing a sustainable future. Implementation of sustainability was a recommendation from the UNCED conference at Rio. At that conference, the nations signed an Agenda 21 to establish 2 new international agencies, one is the International Environmental Agency which would set international standards for exposures to hazardous materials, to be respected by every nation. The second recommendation was an International Environmental Court, a specialised sub-court of the International Court of Justice. I am also recommending the establishment of a World Institute of Sustainable Energy, an neutral international agency open to all energy options.

Thank you very much.

The President :

I Thank you very much, Dr. Bertell.

2. THE ACCIDENT AND ITS IMPLICATIONS FOR OTHER NUCLEAR REACTORS

Speakers :　　Dr. Sergii Mirnyi,　Engineer, Physico-Chemist, Director of Scientific and International Relations for the International Poster and Graphics Exhibition dedicated to Chernobyl. Liquidator.

Professor Vesily Nesterenko, Physicist, Belarusian Research Technical Center, Institute of Radiation Safety, Head for Belarus of the Independent Expert Committee : "Three State Inquiry into the Consequences of the Chernobyl Disaster".

Commander Robert Green, Royal Navy (retired).

Professor Yuli Andreev, Physicist, Liquidator.

Professor Ross Hesketh, Physicist, Berkeley Nuclear Laboratory of the Central Generating Board (CEGB retired.)

Dr. Wolfgang Kromp, Physicist, Nuclear Adviser to the Austrian Federal Chancellor.

The President

I now give the floor to Dr. Sergii Mirnyi.

Dr. Sergii Mirnyi :

In the first part of my presentation I will speak about issues of contamination from a general outlook on the problem. I discovered with astonishment, that in this honourable gathering, I am the only representative of the people, who were not experts in this field in 1986, who didn't deal with nuclear issues, but who were just citizens of the country and are the first victims of the disaster as it stands now.

On the other hand I am a representative of Ukraine which was where the nuclear power plant exploded, and as such I would like to present my outlook 10 years after the event.

In 1986, still in the Soviet Union, I received a military speciality. As my training was in physical chemistry, I was named "commander in a radiation and chemical surveillance platoon" and worked as a so-called "liquidator" in Chernobyl.

What I witnessed there was really incredible for one who was not trained to deal with such events. It is still incredible because, although we are mostly speaking about radiation issues, the main effect of Chernobyl is not solely an atomic issue, it is an atomic-social issue, a radio-social issue. This is the principal consequence.

Radiation workers were unique witnesses of the event. In their ordinary everyday work, they covered a huge territory, from the distance of up to 100 km from the actual reactor. We surveyed a huge territory, and what is equally important is that we surveyed the levels of radiation received by the people.

On behalf of all those people, of whom I am the only representative present here, I demand justice before this Tribunal, justice not only in order to punish the people which were responsible for this catastrophe, but justice for the sake of a real understanding of the events, to prevent future events of this kind. Justice in order to help the real victims of the events, the present victims and the victims who will appear in the future.

I would also like to make some introductory remarks on our hearing. In a few minutes we will start to speak about medical issues, and one of the most important problems will be the doses of radiation received. Let me say that as an insider of the event, I noticed that a proper dose registration was not organised in the zone.

Whenever the doctors or scientists deal with dose-dependent effects, it's science, it's medicine, it's biology. Whenever they deal with doses, they deal with social issues. The doses which were documented in the zone were not recorded as they would have been in a laboratory. I have checked a lot of scientific publications about the medical effects of Chernobyl and in 100 percent of those publications, the dose was reconstructed according to the official data. I witnessed that the real doses were higher than those officially recorded. I was also a witness to medical experiments undertaken on the people, people who were not volunteers, people who were drafted to serve in the military service. Because of the time limit I will not talk a lot about it now, but will discuss this point later in the agenda.

On the effects of contamination, it was considered officially that in the case of an atomic bomb, we would have clear pictures of the contaminated areas. The picture of the contamination after American explosions in Nevada, looks like an octopus, with predictable traces of radiation. When I measured practical day to day levels, I drew a pattern that looked like a mountain, a radioactive Everest. On top of this mountain was the concentrated area around the reactor, from this centre went a long thin trace, another was broader and covered the whole of eastern Belarus, where we checked the villages.

From my point of view, the South and the East were not affected that much, but this was the picture drawn by the commander of a radiation organisms platoon. By analysing the data more closely, it appeared to me that there existed Chernobyl related radiation everywhere.

I hope that this picture will help us to understand the nature of the contamination. According to my results, the first victims of the disaster were the people, they were affected cruelly and directly by direct and indirect, internal and external radiation. The second victims of the radiation were the soils. It appears that years after the disaster the upper 5-10 centimetres of the soils absorbed the radionuclides. They did not allow most of them to go deeper because of their remobilisation (i.e. by annual spring floods).

But as the years pass, the third victims of the radiation appears to be the bottom sediments and the water, the water tables and the water of the rivers. Year by year, according to the research conducted especially by Dr. E. Yakovlev, who has unfortunately been unable to testify before this Tribunal, the radiation sweeps from one water basin to the other, down the river Dnieper.

It is important to emphasise that one of the main radionuclides is radioactive Strontium, which is absorbed in the bones, where it acts selectively on the processes of blood production, so even small doses are extremely dangerous. You know that the river Dnieper gives drinking water to two thirds of the Ukrainian population, so you can imagine the scale of the catastrophe. We can therefore consider that the fourth victim is Mother Earth herself.

According to my own experience, at the time we were only allowed to see what was allowed by the authorities. Scientists were allowed to take samples of the soil only after it was checked and if it was more or less safe. From my experience, even in a contaminated area, the contamination is not uniform, sometimes it may be more or less radioactive, there exist hot spots of radiation, as the radiation erupted out of the reactor by air and fell on certain spots, sometimes 50, 60, 70 km away from the reactor in every direction.

I would like to emphasise two main ideas. Firstly, when dealing with Chernobyl, we should understand that radiation is extremely selective and not uniform in its distribution in space nor in the organism. Secondly, I am convinced that Chernobyl and nuclear issues lack adequate cultural environment. Let me explain this : experts are experts in separate fields, and experts very often cannot understand each other. We need to create a cultural environment around this or that narrow field. This environment can bring about a process of mutual understanding and involvement of ordinary people. This situation will not change as long as it is only spoken of in a language that ordinary people cannot understand.

This could be a sort of bomb shell, because when things will be expressed in a simple, understandable language, this could drive our modern civilisation's thinking up to a point, where such kind of disasters will be avoidable.

I thank you.

The President :

Thank you very much, Dr. Mirnyi.

I now give the floor to Professor Vesily Nesterenko.

Professor Vesily Nesterenko :

Ladies and Gentlemen, my task is an easy one because my paper has been published by a special independent committee. 200 scientists from Belarus, Russia, and Ukraine, among them Professor Burlakova from Moscow and Dr. Yakovlev from Kiev, participated in a common study. Unfortunately their report is only published in Russian at this stage. However a summary has been published in English and German, thanks to Ms. Susan Boos. I present this summary to the Tribunal.

What are the consequences of the Chernobyl disaster for

25

Belarus ? A major part of the country is contaminated. More than 2 million people live on this contaminated land, and more than 130,000 have been resettled to the North of the country. But people still continue to live in 3,000 contaminated villages. The same is true for Russia and Ukraine.

Those people continue to eat food grown in contaminated areas, which represents the greatest problem. Their cumulative dose of radionuclides is growing day by day through food intake.

Our institute, which is a free, non governmental institution, developed a special method to check food for radionuclides. There exists a network of more than 370 centers, where the people can check their food. A special computer accumulates all the information on food contamination for whole Belarus. This allows us to publish maps of the contamination of food, not of the soils, because contaminated food happens to be the greatest problem today. We find quite often levels of contamination that are 10 times higher than those published by the government.

It is very important to mention that over the 5 years, since these centres have been in existence, the level of contamination has not decreased. 70-80% of all radioactivity is taken up by people through food, which is the greatest problem. Each year we publish a special report, about 100 pages, on the food contamination. We publish the list of people who drink contaminated milk, with their names and addresses, and also a list of people who live in highly contaminated areas.

Thus, people have the possibility to know with certainty that it is dangerous to grow and to eat the food in regions situated as far as 200 km away from Chernobyl. I want to give an example : 400 km from the nuclear power station I know a village in the Brest region, where 1,500 adults and 400 children live. According to our standards, the children should not be allowed to drink milk contaminated by more than 37 picoCurie/kg. I mention milk because it is the most highly contaminated food which people consume daily. Unfortunately, in this village, the contamination of the milk is 200 times higher than allowed by the standard.

The children from this particular village were examined by special medical equipment to check the dose level of the different radionuclides : We found a cumulative dose for

Cesium 137 of more than 1000 Becquerels per kilogram. This explains why, according to medical examinations, there is not a single child among the 400 children who live in this village, who is, in reality, quite healthy. Unfortunately this is not the only village in the same situation. I know personally of more than 500 such villages.

As we have not been able to check the food in all the villages situated in the contaminated zones, there might even be many more. Among the milk samples people of the Brest region managed to bring to our centers for checking, only 33 % were under the official standards. 67% were more radioactive than the standards, and 30% of all samples reached 1000 Bq/kg Cs 137. Unfortunately neither the local authorities nor the central government take any notice of our measures, nor act accordingly to improve the situation.

I am a physicist, but I work very closely with physicians. I am very worried about some medical data published in our study. Dr. Bertell just mentioned the kinds of radiation-induced illnesses accepted by the IAEA authorities and I want to compare them with what is observed in 2 highly contaminated areas, Gomel and Moghilev. The Genetic Institute in Minsk collected data from 1982 to 1985, that means before the Chernobyl catastrophe. They have noted in Gomel and Moghilev a significant increase, up to 6 times, of some congenital deformities, which have roughly doubled in the whole country. The IAEA has not acknowledged this.

In highly contaminated areas, a whole range of radiation-induced illnesses, which are not regarded as such by the IAEA, are increased. There exists a special register in the Institute of Radiation in Belarus, updated by 35 specialists who record specific diseases. I will just mention Prof. Kovachenko, a specialist of neurological disorders in children, who found all kinds of psychological and psychiatric disorders. I present here his study to the Tribunal. The most important is that he was able to show that the psychiatric disorders are caused by organic deficiencies. They are not caused by stress or radiophobia, but have an organic background. His study concerns people having been exposed to radiation, 42 people from 4 contaminated areas who suffer from different mental disorders. Mental defects are apparently caused by Chernobyl.

In 3 or 4 generations, in his opinion as an expert, there might be nobody left to monitor such processes !

<u>The President :</u>

Thank you very much, Professor Nesterenko.

I now give the floor to Commander Robert Green.

<u>Commander Robert Green :</u>

I would like to thank the organisers of this important Tribunal for inviting me to speak here today. I am not a qualified scientist or engineer, let alone a nuclear specialist. My role is that of a scribe and messenger - and I am aware of the hazards for messengers who carry bad news.

My task is to introduce the paper, co-written by Don Arnott and myself, called : "Chernobyl, Unique Safety Valve for a Reactor Nuclear Explosion". Don is 74 years old and disabled, so unfortunately he is not able to be here. With an honours degree in chemistry and zoology, he was recruited in 1942 into what became Amersham International, where he worked on making luminescent paint from radium for instrument panels. After Hiroshima and Nagasaki, he decided to focus on radio-medicine. He worked on thyroid studies, first at the Medical Research Council, London, and then as head of the radio-isotope laboratories at the London Hospital, researching anti-thyroid drugs. In the 1960's he did work for the IAEA, including writing a handbook on medical uses of radioisotopes.

On retirement, he became an adviser in UK, to anti-nuclear campaigners, including my late aunt Hilda Murrell. After she was murdered in 1984, I met him. We collaborated on presenting evidence on nuclear reactor safety at the Hinkley Point Public Inquiry (1988-89) into the proposed second UK Pressurised Water Reactor.

The Hinkley Inquiry Report, published in 1990, showed wide disagreement about the cause and nature of the Chernobyl explosion, which was unresolved. In discussion with me, Don explained as a chemist why he believed it must have been a nuclear explosion - which had not been raised at the Inquiry. We could find no mention of this anywhere. He then realised that the energy from a nuclear explosion could never be contained - on the contrary - it would be increased by attempts to contain it. He therefore concluded that the RBMK containment design, with its loose-fitting pile cap, was paradoxically safer than most Western designs. This was the reason why the energy was released with minimum damage, such that the adjacent Unit 3 kept running for over 3 hours before being shut down. In any multi-reactor site of Western design, there would be much more damage with high risk of one or more other reactors exploding.

We were fortunate to find the Spanish analysis by Martinez-Val et al, which established the mechanism for the nuclear explosion. For this we are indebted to Zhores Medvedev, who was advising us before Professor Ross Hesketh got involved.

It remained for us to identify a scenario for a nuclear explosion in each of the current Western reactor designs. Here we were helped by Dr. Richard Webb, a US nuclear physicist and engineer, who had worked with Admiral Rickover on the prototype PWR at Shippingport. I had sponsored him as my second expert witness at Hinkley.

May I take this opportunity to thank Professor Ross Hesketh for his supportive peer review, of which I have copies. He was the only qualified nuclear scientist we could find, who was prepared to do it. Without him, we would not have been able to convince the National Steering Committee of UK Nuclear Free Local Authorities to challenge the Health & Safety Executive with our findings, which I would now like to summarise.

I will just briefly go through them.

1. Chernobyl was primarily a nuclear explosion.

2. No containment could have withstood such a powerful explosion.

3. The loose fitting, 2,000 tons RBMK pile cap, acted in effect as a "safety valve", by prematurely terminating the chain reaction. This reduced the energy of the explosion and hence fission product release. It also confined the damage to Unit 4, sparing the three adjacent reactors and two highly radioactive spent fuel stores.

4. A pressurised, integral containment - as in all British, in fact all Western thermal reactors - would have increased the violence of the explosion.

5. At least one scenario exists for a nuclear explosion in

British Advanced Gas-cooled Reactors, (AGR), Pressurised Water Reactors (PWR) and for the Dounreay Fast Breeder Reactor.

The official UK Report :

- refuses to admit that the primary cause was a nuclear explosion;

- wrongly maintains instead that it was primarily a steam explosion;

- does not explain why there were two explosions;

- gives no figure for the actual energy release in each explosion;

- states that the RBMK pile cap weighed only 1000 tons, half the latest official Russian figure;

- does not explain why the adjacent Unit 3 and shared spent fuel store suffered so little damage that the former kept operating for 3 1/2 hours after the explosion;

- fails to mention that no containment could have withstood such an explosion;

- ignores the fact that there exist nuclear weapons with smaller energy yields than that experienced during the Chernobyl nuclear explosion, where the yield was just under 0.3 kilotons;

- omits to point out that the potential radioactive contamination from Unit 4 (and any other larger reactor) is hundreds of times greater than that from Hiroshima/Nagasaki atomic bombs;

The significance of all this is particularly interesting for the UK industry - but for the West as well.

Our paper argues that the UK nuclear power industry refuses to concede that a nuclear explosion is possible in a reactor because :

- even a tiny, inefficient nuclear explosion in a reactor would be many times more powerful than a chemical one, and would therefore spread more radioactive contamination over a wider area;

- it would correctly link commercial atomic reactors with nuclear weapons in the public opinion, and thus irreparably damage the industry's credibility and image;

30

- if the industry could not refute the possibility of a nuclear explosion in any of the Western reactor designs, AGR, PWR and Dounreay's FBR, these designs could not satisfy the British Nuclear Industry's Safety Assessment Principle 152, which states :

"The containment should adequately contain such radioactive matter as may be released into it as a result of any fault in the reactor."

- hence the AGRs and Dounreay FBR would have to be shut down as soon as possible, and the construction of Sizewell B stopped.

Don has also asked me to stress the postscript, to which he would like to add evidence from Margaret Gowing's history of the British nuclear industry called "Britain and Atomic Energy 1947-1952". I would like to quote two short extracts. They concern the reasons for Britain adopting a gas-cooled, rather than a water-cooled, graphite-moderated reactor design. On page 382, describing the US water-cooled graphite-moderated pile at Hanford :

"Because of the risks in the event of an accident, the pile must be at a remote site. For water absorbs neutrons, so that if the flow of water were interrupted and the control and safety rods failed to operate immediately, the water in the cooling annulus would evaporate and would no longer be there to absorb neutrons. Those neutrons would then be available to multiply the rate of fission in the pile, which would become violently supercritical; the temperature would rise, the fuel elements would vaporise and radioactivity would be widely scattered."

Then on page 385 is the statement:

"Gas-cooling removes the danger of violent supercriticality.."

So awareness of the danger of a nuclear explosion from graphite-moderation with water-cooling is as old as reactor theory itself.

There is one new factor which Don has come up with, which we did not include in our paper - and Martinez-Val missed it as well. We contend it may be the final nail in the coffin of the nuclear industry's claim that a steam explosion was the primary cause. Each coolant tube has a safety valve to release automatically excess steam pressure. The crucial point is that they are positioned above the pile cap and below the charge face. What is more, steam was seen lifting the fuel channel caps on the charge face, just before the first explosion.

Thank you.

The President :

I thank you, Commander Green.

We now come to the comments by the expert's panel, and I give the floor to Professor Yuli Andreev.

Professor Yuli Andreev :

Honourable Judges, Ladies and Gentlemen, I planned to make my statement in a certain way, but the last statement of Commander Green changed my intentions a little. I can add to the statement of Commander Green. What I have seen confirms his theory, which seems to me very important.

From the roof of the Chernobyl unit number 4, I have seen the elements of nuclear fuel, which were damaged from inside. I believe this totally confirms his theory about a nuclear explosion, because it requires only common sense to understand that during a steam explosion, or any other chemical explosion, the elements cannot be damaged from inside.

I must state here that during my 4 years of teaching in the University of Vienna, I teach my students that the Chernobyl catastrophe was caused by a nuclear blast, and that any other definition represents some kind of euphemism, probably uttered with criminal intentions. This is the first part of my statement.

The second part is connected with the persons whom I consider responsible for the victims of Chernobyl. Today it's no more under discussion - we observe in Chernobyl significant quantities of thyroid cancers in the children.

I must give here a small explanation. I am an expert in emergency services, and I spent 5 years in Chernobyl, from the 28th of May 1986 till December 1991. I know the circumstances connected with this accident and I have the information about the activities of the persons who were responsible for the elimination of consequences, for the emergency. Among them I must remember Mr. Israel, who is a Russian Academician. At the time of the Chernobyl accident, he was the President of the USSR Meteorological Service, and he was directly responsible for the prevention of the radiological impact on the local population including children.

I testify that the proper measures were not undertaken in this case. Those measures were extremely simple, it was necessary to keep children at home, not to permit them to go on the street, to keep the windows shut, and this during two weeks. This might have resulted in the absence of so many thyroid cancers among the children. Consequently I consider that Mr. Israel is personally responsible for the harm done to the children. Yesterday Mr. Israel made one of his statements in the IAEA and he did not mention his responsibility. I think this is not a proper behaviour for this scientist. This brings to its end my statement on the circumstances of the Chernobyl accident.

Additionally, I will try to use this forum to express some of my general considerations.

As a specialist in the emergency service, I think that a risky facility must be defined as a facility that possesses a dangerous inventory, together with the energy to distribute this inventory. I think that if such a definition would be taken in account, there would be no Chernobyl, no Bhopal, or no other nuclear accidents. But because commercial, and sometimes political interests are opposed to such a definition, Chernobyl and Three Mile Island were possible.

Why do we allow such a situation in our world where we do not even have any proper definition of our industrialism ? I think it is because of some kind of degradation of modern science and modern technology. Contrary to what it was, say 100 years ago, science has now become a profession which is controlled by the commercial and political interests. Until this situation changes for the better, we will live under the threat of great disaster. I believe that the main lesson of Chernobyl concerns not only the nuclear arena. Chernobyl taught us that in the future even more dangerous accidents are possible, if we don't change our way of behaviour.

The President :

Thank you Professor Andreev.

I now give the floor to Professor Hesketh.

Professor Ross Hesketh :

Mr. President, members of the Jury, I would like to echo the words of the previous speaker and I would like also to return to the introductory remarks of Dr. Tognoni on the lack of accountability of the nuclear industry, and also on the fact that such accidents are indicators of structures of society, and on the place of several industries within society.

It seems to me that the significance of the Chernobyl accident, as an indicator of the structure of our society, is at least as important, and especially as the previous speaker said, for future accidents, as the accident itself. I would like to draw the attention of the Jury to the causes of the accident. We have met today to consider primarily the effects of the accident and the health effects. I'm not competent to discuss the health effects, but I have paid some attention to the causes of the accident. Many people in the industry recognise that there were 2 explosions in Unit 4 at Chernobyl. Many people who recognise this in private conversations, are continuing to declare in their public statements that those explosions were non-nuclear in nature.

As to the explosions themselves and to the matter of accountability, the Jury will recall that during the 1986 Review Conference, the operators of Chernobyl 4 were blamed for the disaster, and the chief engineer at Chernobyl 4th block remained in prison for several years. In 1990, Mr. Gorbatchev formed a committee with experts chosen from outside the nuclear industry, and it produced a report which I think is vital in this context. The report of the Glasnost Committee, appears not as the prime document in the booklet published by the Atomic Energy Authority, it appears as Annex 1. Annex 1 is the longest document in the book and it is in my view the most important, because it removes the responsibility formerly attributed to the operators of Chernobyl, and it repeats many times that the operators were not responsible for the accident. I have summarised this in two documents for the Court.

According to the Glasnost Committee, the responsibility of the explosion rests with the chief design engineer, the general designers, the scientific manager, the USSR Ministry of Intermediate Sized Machinery, the USSR Ministry of Power and the Soviet Regulatory Authority.

You will see that the operators of Chernobyl 4 are not listed. You will also realise that the 6 parties that I have just mentioned have received no censure for the accident at Chernobyl. Moreover, heavy criticism of the operators continues to appear in the Western press, and I don't know, but imagine in the Eastern press as well. Recently I read, for example, that the graves of those operators of Chernobyl 4, who died and are buried in the cemetery, are now being desecrated by those who hold them responsible for the accident. This seems to me the most unacceptable effect of propaganda that one can imagine. It reveals some of the structural defects in our societies, that Dr. Tognoni was talking about.

I would invite the Jury to consider what I think is one of the most important documents in regard to the cause of the Chernobyl accident, that is the report published as Annex 1 in this IAEA document I give to the Court. To conclude my comments, I would repeat that in 1990, the Committee appointed by Mr. Gorbatchev cleared the operators of any responsibility for the accident. Unfortunately, in the subsequent 4 years, the nuclear industry has first gradually, and then more strongly, reattributed that same accusation for the accident to the operators. If you look at reports appearing now, certainly from the House of Commons in Britain, you will find that the operators, once more, are fiercely blamed.

Thank you.

The President :

Thank you, Professor Hesketh.

I would now like to invite questions from the Jury to the experts.

Judge Freda Meissner-Blau :

Could you please specify in which respect you consider the accident as an indicator of the structure of our society ?

Professor Ross Hesketh :

The prime physical cause of the accident lies in a design fault in the reactor system. That design fault had been recognised in December 1983 in two reactors in Lithuania, and had also been observed at Unit 4 at Chernobyl. Therefore there is no doubt that the design fault was known. The severity of the design fault was also known. It was known that if you took the control rods out, you had an extremely dangerous condition where the reactor could be blown up by the emergency protection, which in other words, instead of protecting the reactor, would blow it up, and this is in fact what happened. It should be the oldest rule in the book that you do not design an emergency protection system which can go into reverse, and destroy that which you are trying to protect. Now I think that the fact that such a situation can persist for 3 years, known to people at the top of the industry, known to the ministries concerned, with nothing being done about it, represents a symptom of the place taken by the industry in our society.

Professor Yuli Andreev :

Maybe I can add something on the circumstances connected with the responsibility of the operators. The fact that the operators were not responsible for the accident was known immediately after the accident, and even before the accident. Maybe it is not a well known fact, but before this accident, a letter was written by one of the operators of the nuclear power plant to the top establishment of the USSR nuclear industry. In this letter the future accident was described. The main error made by the nuclear establishment in the case of this nuclear accident, was that the possibility of the nuclear blast had never been explained to the operators, in spite of the fact that the designers knew it exactly. This dysfunction is not specific for the Soviet nuclear industry. As I understand it now, the same situation is possible in any big industrial facility, not only nuclear, when commercial considerations prevail on security considerations. This could surely be analysed in detail, but now we have no time to go deeper into it.

The President :

Thank you.

Dr. Wolfgang Kromp from Vienna who has to leave very soon, has asked to be allowed to take the floor now. Please take the floor, Dr. Kromp.

Dr. Wolfgang Kromp :

Honourable Judges, dear Audience, I am very honoured to contribute to this extraordinary event. I was called to give some comments on these problems. This is certainly a very difficult task, and I'm not so sure that I will be able to do so. I would like to direct your attention on factors, which in my opinion are the real causes, although they are not stated officially, accessible, or easily understandable.

In my opinion it is not possible to isolate, to judge and charge the people who work in nuclear power plants and in the nuclear industry. For me, those activities of complicated organisations are comparable to mushrooms. Everybody knows that a mushroom is not something that is standing alone, it is just the visible part of something which is much larger, and might penetrate the whole wood. This is what concerns me. We should not be ready to accuse and charge individuals or singular parts of our society.

To some extent, we are part of the same society and we also add to the problems of our society. As to Professor Israel, we don't know how much he was informed about the measurements of radiation, we don't know what his constraints were, his role and his degree of being a prisoner in his own society. We don't know these things exactly.

When people try to accuse, in an unjustified way, people such as the operators of the Chernobyl reactor, the very first task for our Judges should be to clear those people from this accusation.

I would like to give an example of how you and I contribute. We are all trained to operate vehicles, automobiles, and we all know that sometimes the emergency system of an automobile, which are the brakes, in some circumstances, when driving on a slippery road, can lead to dangers. We know what could occur if we used the brakes improperly, we could create a big disaster. In some circumstances it is better not to use the brakes or to use the brakes very cautiously. So we are all trained to operate things which are convenient, but which have similar features as this reactor. We should as a consequence not be astonished that our society allows these dangerous facilities to go on, even knowing of their dangers. We do not really object to the car in our society for example.

This is why I am hesitating to judge and blame the people in this part of our society. The problem is much deeper and much more extended, and we have to focus on the whole system which is running in a very bad direction.

For instance take the IAEA meeting on Chernobyl. You see on one side those who apparently have grasped the full consequences of this disaster. One was talking about the 35,000 invalids he has to deal with, the other one was talking about the consequences on agriculture and on environment, another was talking about spending a quarter of the gross national product in dealing with this disaster, attempting to improve the situation. This is one part of the people attending this meeting.

On the other side, the majority of the scientists, members of the IAEA or associated with it, either do not see these problems or they touch them marginally or do not see the real causes, they see every other cause except the radiation. This is also an indication that our society, its whole structure, is not working. We have to investigate this, to find out the causes, in which way we are contributing ourselves to this kind of society. This is why I would recommend to be very cautious when condemning, accusing and charging people, we have to look for the roots, which apparently, lie much deeper.

I would like to present some positive views on what could be done. I am a scientist, I'm not speaking as an advisor to the Austrian Chancellor - I'm speaking here as a private person, and as a citizen who tries to use his common sense. We must reform our education system, our universities and our schools. We have to improve our scientific system, this was evident when listening to this IAEA Conference.

We must try to find out a proper system of facts-recording, when looking for the causes. We must stop educating highly specialised experts in narrow areas, unaware of the whole picture, not seeing the harm they are causing. We have to improve this system in order to be able to trust each other, to find a common language.

We also have to educate ourselves and our expert scientists to find a language with which we can speak to the people, understandable to everybody, journalists, politicians. Then everyone could inform themselves correctly on every project on the agenda, like the construction of a dangerous facility with only one-sided benefits, which more or less

can be estimated, and high danger potentials, wh
normally cannot be estimated properly, as nobody rea...
knows the risk of nuclear power plants.

We have to develop an educational democratic process for
the whole community, which participates not only in the
benefits but also in the risks. It is the only way we have to
get out of this mess. This is a complicated process, and we
are not yet very far into it, we are just at the beginning.

Thank you.

The President :

I thank you very much, Dr. Kromp.

Now we shall continue with the questions from the Judges.

Judge Surendar Gadekar :

I have a question to Professor Hesketh.

You said that the default of the reactor was known and that
nevertheless, the operators have been allowed to operate
it. Is this the case for all other reactors ?

Are there other reactors with structures that could lead to
accidents of this nature?

Professor Ross Hesketh :

In general, regarding the inventory of dangerous materials,
from the general point of view of radiation - there is no
difference between the different types of reactors. This is
my fundamental point of view.

The basic safety assessment is a method which permits to
calculate the risks and the extent of damages. I cannot
elaborate on this point, but I believe that the classical
methods of risk assessment are absolutely incorrect. Why ?

You can only assess risks by using objective data on known
accidents. Every nuclear engineer knows that man is the
most dangerous factor in nuclear accidents, as man is
absolutely unpredictable. This is why all risks assessments
are totally biased.

This brings me back to my first statement : no reactor is
safe.

<u>Judge Freda Meissner-Blau :</u>

This may seem a very blunt question, but I understand that you worked in the Berkeley nuclear laboratories - would you be in favour of stopping alltogether the nuclear industry?

<u>Professor Ross Hesketh :</u>

I want to meet my answer to that question with the question put by Judge Gadekar, as to all nuclear reactors being dangerous, but not in the same way.

The fault which destroyed Chernobyl 4 is probably unique to the system of graphite-gas moderated reactors. This system can go into reverse. This means that the emergency protection system can go into reverse, and there exists no other reactor types where this can happen. The RMBK system in Chernobyl is of course not an unique system. The Americans built a very similar system at Hanford to produce Plutonium, they are essentially Plutonium producing reactors, which is their primary function.

There are other defects in other reactors types. It would be too long to enumerate them. Commander Green has pointed out one difference in western reactors : if you look at a western commercial reactor, you find that its control rods are made of less expensive material, with a very low melting point (Cadmium-Silver-Indium alloy). If anything goes wrong with such reactors, the control rods are the first things to melt. In an accident, it would be likely that you would loose the control rods before you lost the core.

The problem with accidents is that it is very difficult to envisage them beforehand. The thing that is prominent about Chernobyl, is that everything had been envisaged before the accident. I open this book at a page which tells me that the design defect, which actually destroyed the reactor, was known two and a half years before Chernobyl, now that's not my words, that's printed on this page. Dr. Iakimets just reminded me a moment ago that there was a very similar accident at Leningrad 1 in 1975, so 11 years before Chernobyl, the defect was known.

You asked if I would close down all nuclear power stations ? As a nuclear technologist, I do not want to be the one who simply breaks up the machinery.

40

The problem I see is that nuclear power is out of c⌐
When we look at the safeguards issued to prevent nuc⌐
materials from the civil industry being used in nuclear
weapons, you will find that those safeguards are verified
by the nuclear industry themselves, they are handled by the
people being safeguarded. This is like asking Chicago
gangsters policing themselves, and this I think is the
answer. You can have a society in which there is a police
force, but there is no use in asking the gangsters to be the
police.

The President :

It seems to me that 2 themes have arisen, firstly the
evaluation of the damages, and there seems to have been an
underestimation of the damages received.

The other one is the problem of causes, and there also
seems to be some disagreement between people who
consider that the nuclear industry in the western world is
totally safe, and people who are against that opinion.

In face of such disagreements between scientists, is there a
forum where it is possible to discuss such divergent
opinions, or do we always speak with those who agree with
us, with the consequence of two entirely separated
discourses ? Is it possible to bring them together ?

Dr. Rosalie Bertell :

I think that the structure in which the nuclear dialogue has
taken place excludes any common forum.

I recall that when there's a meeting of the IAEA, you can't
even attend unless you are sent by your government. For
example in the USA, it would be the Department of Energy
(DoE), who would decide whether or not you could go to a
meeting. If you are a dissenter you are not sent to the
meeting. When Bernd Franke attended for the first time as a
German delegate, there was a great uproar in the IAEA.
They announced that it was the first time that the anti-
nuclear argument had got into their meeting.

The ICRP is self-constituted, 13 members of the main
committee make all the decisions, they appoint themselves.
They originally formed a group. New members have to be
approved by the group, there is no outsider, even the WHO
as such can't put anybody on ICRP, they are very tight
nuclear friends.

ICRP considers itself as speaking for the consensus of the scientific opinion. In 1989 many of the people who are here now, helped to collect a petition, we had over 800 signatures from physicians, scientists and Nobel laureates, trying to get ICRP to lower the permissible recommended radiation exposure. And even in the face of a petition signed by over 800 internationally known scientists, they still claimed that they represented the consensus of the scientific opinion. It's been very difficult.

The President:

Do you think that there exists some kind of collective responsibility of the scientific community or not ?

Commander Robert Green :

Well I'm not a scientist, just an ordinary citizen, but I have detected, in my brief time of campaigning against nuclear power in the UK, the ability of the nuclear industry to isolate themselves from discussion. We have had moments when we've been able to engage them in open correspondence. One of the moments was at the Hinkley Point Inquiry, where you could write a letter to them, asking a question. For the first time your letter was published as an inquiry document, and so the whole inquiry knew they had been asked this question. Therefore they had to reply, and they had to reply quickly. That was the only forum that I've come across where you have been able to get information out of them, and you could see that they were extremely uncomfortable in that environment.

Otherwise, the difficulty is that they will just stonewall on you, they will debate it for a while, but there is a moment where they will just shut down. Somehow we have to go around that to the ordinary people.

I am not a scientist, but I found a scientist, Don Arnott, who could explain things to me, in understandable terms for me, and I do not think I am exceptional in any way. I find a great problem in journalists who glaze over when you mention the word nuclear, there is a mystique about nuclear themes, where they feel that it is beyond them.

I think this is something we should work on, it's a question of language, it's a question of education and helping them, and getting them to get into the subject and do their

homework on this. I believe that there is a very s
need for this. Even now, in reports on Chernobyl in s
newspapers in UK, enormous errors are being made, basi
errors which are not being picked up, so the confusion
continues.

Professor Ross Hesketh :

What Dr. Bertell has said about representatives who are not
approved by the industry, who are being refused a platform
from which to speak, is abundantly true from my
experience and many other's.

If you wish for example to work in the IAEA, you have to
have the explicit approval, or recommendation of your own
domestic atomic energy authority. The idea that the IAEA is
in some way an objective body, separated from the atomic
industry, is a complete nonsense, it has absolutely no
foundation.

There is a difficulty for people in the nuclear industry,
which is by no means unique to this industry, that is that
their career prospects are dependent on saying what their
employers want to hear. This is part of the structural
problems of our society. It happened recently in the UK with
regard to mad cow disease, where scientists, who some
years ago said there was a problem that needed to be
tackled urgently, have lost their research grants. A society
that says : "I want a scientist but s/he must say what I
want to hear", is a society in which there is something
very fundamentally wrong.

To answer your question, unless that societal disease can
be cured, I think the whole nuclear industry should be shut
down, because we are all in such immense danger.

Judge Corinne Kumar:

I want to thank very specially, every one of you who
brought your testimony to this Tribunal. I will try to
connect by way of comment some of the questions I would
like to put to all of you.

When we talk about accidents as being part of structures,
we speak of structural violence. My question is following :
is this related to a world view, or cosmology, that
encapsulates rationality and scientificity, a cosmology that
allows us a distance and an objectivity, that allows us to

make the atomic and hydrogen bomb, not taking into account the social and violent consequences ?

My question is : is this discourse already flawed by notions of scientificality and rationality, which we in the PPT, as alternative thinkers, must object to in order to seek justice ? My question is : do we need to change the parameters of that discourse, the violence of science, the violence of the development model, the violence of nuclear energy and nuclear weapons ? One witness talked about these really being experiments on people. When we think of the atomic and hydrogen bomb tests in the Marshall Islands in 1954, that Dr. Bertell spoke of, and how for years the US said that this was an accident, that the direction of the wind had changed, when in reality it was a scientific experiment on people that were dispensable.

Where do we take nation states that violate the sovereignty of peoples ? Where do we take them to task ? Where can the people of the Pacific go against the nation state of the US ? where can Tahiti go against France ? and where can the people of Chernobyl go, and against whom ?

The President :

This is a very difficult but very interesting question.

Judge Surendar Gadekar :

My question is for Professor Hesketh. In France they rely on nuclear power for commercial electricity, I think at the level of 75 % at the moment. Do you know if they have worked out a concrete agenda, or is there anyone who has worked out a concrete agenda to move from the current reliance on the nuclear energy to a soft energy path ? As someone who has been engaged in the peace movement, I am always asked if we have worked out a concrete agenda to get rid of nuclear weapons from earth, yes we have. In the case of nuclear energy, is there a concrete agenda ?

Commander Robert Green :

Yes, such an agenda exists, worked out by an engineers office (Inestène, France).

Professor Yuli Andreev :

As an engineer, I have always tried to be practical. In spite of our best intentions, the existing nuclear power plants will not be shut down tomorrow. It's economically impossible. We have become hostages of our own technological solutions. I think that our activity must be not so much on shutting down existing power plants but our activity must be more wise. We must prevent the future development of this energy.

Today it is nuclear energy which appears to be extremely dangerous, but tomorrow it could be other types of technologies : genetic technology, fusion, or some unknown technologic developments.

If we do not force today, by democratic methods, our legislators to edict rules to limit the ability of the big industrial structures to develop their benefits, disregarding the human well-being, we will lose our battle.

Professor Ross Hesketh:

I personally have no plan neither concrete proposal to shut down the nuclear industry, either tomorrow or next week.

I would like to link this question to the previous one, about cosmological views, referring to the world in which we live. Besides the nuclear industry, there exist in the UK a whole range of alternative sources : wave machines, wind machines, specifically non-nuclear sources. A committee was set up in the 70's to develop them. It spent the first ten years showing why non-nuclear methods of generating energy would not work. When there was a scheme that did work, this committee falsified the figures, falsified the price of steel by a factor of ten, which was visible for anyone to see. But this was pushed through the committee which crushed the scheme.

This questions the functioning of our society. It is no use to say : we want alternative energy sources, and then to place the necessary mechanism in the hands of people who are bitterly opposed to alternative sources.

The answer to the question of alternative sources of energy hangs very much on the first - that is, what is our approach ? It is easy to set up committees to promote these sources, if we allow these committees to sabotage them. This is not a problem linked to the nuclear industry alone. Fighting change is part of conservatism, fighting to preserve your industry, regardless of the rest of the society.

Unless we can get to this problem, we will never get concrete alternatives to get rid of nuclear power industry. Technically, it is not too difficult. But you can't do it without a shift in what society is driving at.

The President :

Thank you very much.

Now we have completed the first part of the hearing on the implications of the Chernobyl catastrophe on other reactors and on nuclear industry in general.

We shall come to the second part, which concerns :

3. CHERNOBYL AND THE HUMAN RIGHTS OF THE VICTIMS

Speakers :   *Dr. Irina Grushevaya, Foundation for the Children of Chernobyl, Minsk*

Dr. Yuri Pankratz, Foundation for the Children of Chernobyl, Minsk

Professor Galina Drozdova, Russian People's Friendship University, Moscow

Professor Larissa Skuratovskaya, Institute of General Pathology and Pathophysiology, Russian Academy of Medical Sciences, Moscow

Professor Peter Weish, Member of the Austrian Academy of Sciences, Vienna

Professor Hari Sharma, Nuclear Chemistry, University of Waterloo, Canada, International Medical Commission on Chernobyl

The President :

I give the floor to Dr. Irina Grushevaya from Minsk.

Dr. Irina Grushevaya :

I would like to greet all the participants to this alternative gathering. I am very happy that a voice from Belarus will be heard today. Before Chernobyl, Belarus wasn't so much known in the outer world, it was a white spot on the map. As for ourselves, we didn't realise that our rights had been violated by Chernobyl.

10 years after Chernobyl we know. In our "Foundation for the Children of Chernobyl", we know that a kind of war is going on against the health of our children, against our country and against people living in Belarus. The so-called peaceful atom kills the lives of people. We experience a tragedy : our children, our families are the first victims of Chernobyl, not just for these years, but for many years to come.

Many people discuss Chernobyl as a technical issue. As a mother of two children in Belarus, I know that this is a terrible tragedy for the people. When we read in the newspaper that the biggest catastrophe was just what happened inside the reactor, we protest against this view, because it's a second war waged by the government, the IAEA and some other institutions against the people of Belarus.

Today the rights of people are violated. They have no right to eat clean food, they have no right to get a clear information as to what is really happening, this represents the most dramatic consequence of Chernobyl. 3 years after Chernobyl, from 1986 to 1989, the people of Belarus had no information whatsoever about the kinds of consequences they experienced. There was a black-out, a cover up of all consequences of the catastrophe.

We didn't know that 70 percent of all radioactivity settled on the soil of Belarus, we didn't know that 25 percent of our people lived in contaminated areas, eating contaminated food.

We didn't know that after 6 years, only 16 percent of children born in Moghilev, one of our most contaminated regions, would be healthy.

We didn't know at the time that there would be an increase in about 37 different sicknesses in children. Thanks to the democratic movement in our country, we now have access to that information. For years, many mothers and fathers with small kids visited their grandmothers and grandfathers in highly contaminated areas, because they had no access to information about these areas.

Who are the people responsible for covering up the consequences of Chernobyl ? We know their names. They are presently members of our Parliament and they continue to be the bosses of the environmental and health services, the same people that during the first 4 years, tried to cover up the consequences of the disaster. That is why it's understandable why the government imposes all kinds of obstacles to the people who try to help themselves, organise NGO movements to help children and families.

In 1989, it was very important to listen to the people. The organisers of the "Chernobyl Rally" in 1989 were arrested. Nevertheless we organised our own Tribunal on the Chernobyl crime.

Only in 1991, under the pressure of the non-governmental

movement, the government just began to understand what was happening and took some measures. We managed to get a special law to help the people living in contaminated areas, to have some better situation for the people living in zones contaminated from 1 to 5 Curie per square kilometre.

But two months ago, the government adopted a new law, naming as only the people living in areas contaminated by at least 5 Curie per square kilometre, all the others being considered by the government as living in healthy resorts.

Today the government of Belarus, and Lukashenko declared this himself at the IAEA conference, is encouraging people to move to the contaminated areas as if everything was OK there, and this encouragement is organised on a large scale. This new conception has never been published and was adopted without any discussion, neither in the mass media or in the Academy of Sciences in our country.

In 1992, 1994 and 1996, our "Foundation for the Children of Chernobyl" organised three congresses, "The World After Chernobyl". We wanted to underline that we are the subjects, we the people can help ourselves, we are not objects for the government to undertake all kinds of experiments on us. It was very important for the democracy, for the people, for the public opinion, to proclaim this firmly.

Unfortunately our government, even this year, didn't attend any of those 3 Congresses, although last March, we had 500 guests coming from 39 countries. The government still thinks that our people have no right to be informed on the real consequences of the Chernobyl catastrophe.

We are very thankful to you to help the people from Belarus to hear the voices speaking here. Our work is to give hope to many people, to change their perspectives for the future. I don't want such a future for our children. The consequences of Chernobyl concern radioactivity, but also, and this is very important, disinformation, cover-ups and so on. We must change this situation in order to live in a world that is safe for the children in Belarus.

Thank you very much.

I will now give to the 6 Judges the proceedings of our last Congress, March 1996 in Minsk : "The World after Chernobyl". They contain very precise medical data, and I hope that these documents will help you to issue a very important Verdict next Monday.

<u>The President :</u>

Thank you, Dr. Grushevaya.

I now give the floor to Dr. Yuri Pankratz, from Minsk.

<u>Dr. Yuri Pankratz :</u>

I am very thankful to be able to speak before this Tribunal on behalf of Belarus and of the people of Belarus, who experienced many paradoxes in the history of our country.

We have never had any nuclear power stations on our territory, we have never been aggressive to any nation. Nevertheless, 25% of our people died during the Second World War, and now, 25% of our territory is contaminated by radioactivity. The Belarussian people are very tolerant.

It is very important to note that there are changes for the worse in our government's policy. Our very honourable Judges must know this, and take this into account while formulating their Verdict.

This year and already the year before (1995 and 1996), many of the once evacuated towns and villages are being reoccupied by refugees, fleeing from war zones in the former Soviet Union. This creates a new wave of Chernobyl victims. The main problem is that our government encourages people to live in those contaminated areas.

Irina Grushevaya already pointed out that, notwithstanding the fact that many people already live in contaminated areas, our President, M. Lukashenko made a special speech at the IAEA Conference 3 or 4 days ago. Some of his words are difficult to understand : He said : "We will encourage the people to come back, we will encourage them, we will open the shops again, and make it possible for people to return in evacuated towns and villages".

I think that this is criminal. What is really tragic is that the people are willing to come back, they were never told how dangerous it was, and now with our country experiencing a horrible economic crisis, they have no choice.

When people were settled from highly to less contaminated areas, many psychological mistakes were made by the government : they were not settled village to village, community to community, they were settled at random, family by family. Western people are used to frequent moves, I know that in Canada, families move almost every 5 years. In our country it is customary to stay in one place, and the government takes advantage of this situation, again

50

and again. The President says that it is not dangerous and the people who want to come back, return like sheep in highly contaminated zones.

I want to give to the Judges a special document : we have learned that 10 years after Chernobyl, 26 institutions : orphanages, schools for disabled children, boarding schools, nurseries, schools for deaf children, with altogether 5,026 children, still continue to live in contaminated areas.

This document is very important for us. It may have been difficult to move people, but it is 10 times easier to resettle kindergartens and schools to non-contaminated areas.

I want to present other documents to the Judges. We experience many problems with the humanitarian aid. We managed to get 6,000 tons of humanitarian aid to the Republic of Belarus, we have partners in 26 countries. Some of our partners couldn't send humanitarian aid, because it wasn't officially listed as humanitarian aid, as for example, refrigerators for hospitals. This may appear as a detail, but it's a very important problem.

They sent a special letter to the President of our country and here is a copy. He gave a typical red-tape answer, promising to make all obstacles disappear and allow the refrigerators to be brought in, all humanitarian aid. It was signed December 1, 1995. In 1996, a partner tried 3 times to send those refrigerators to our country. Impossible, nothing had changed.

No measures have been taken to create an international or an interstate legislative base, that would envision compensation of damages and losses caused by the normal operation of power plants, or potential accidents in power plants.

Thanks to Dr. Rosalie Bertell, I visited a nuclear power plant in Toronto, and I spoke to the director of the safety at the plant, he told me many things and he invited me to drink water collected downstream from the power-plant and so on. After one hour I gave him the information I had from Dr. Bertell, and he was very shocked.

The people living 11 km from this nuclear facility in Canada, experience very similar health problems as the Chernobyl victims, although not on the same scale. That is why, when we speak about safety of nuclear power stations we speak of a myth, it is pure nonsense. I asked this man : "What about leakages ?" I told him "I am not Yuri Pankratz, citizen of Belarus, I am God". He was very surprised, because he rarely has the occasion to speak with God at this short distance ! I told him : "Listen, I have no tape-recorder, nothing. What about leakages at your station ?" He looked at me, and there was a pause and then he told me, "We allow some leakages, it's because of the system, it's because its more dangerous not to allow some leakages." And this is the best nuclear power station, advertised all over the world.

This is my answer to some other question about these so-called high-tech best power stations and so on and so forth. Of course the level of risk is different, but there exist no nuclear facilities without risk.

Our "Foundation for the Children of Chernobyl" believes that the profits of atomic energy should be shared, in order to promote alternative sources that are not so expensive. When we talk about cheap nuclear energy, it's a lie. We believe that alternative sources of energy would not be so expensive, if we took some part of the money from nuclear power stations to promote their use.

Our Foundation believes that it is very important to take a good decision on Monday, to establish a new organisation in the framework of the United Nations, where scientists, doctors, physicists, specialists not connected with nuclear power energy would be in control. Without such a control, we will have the same atomic guild, going to the same conferences, inviting only their people who share the same ideas, their friends, with no access for us to these boards in order to change the situation.

I have many other proposals to the Peoples Tribunal, would it be possible to publish the Verdict in many newspapers, maybe some magazines would do it. One of the most important problems is that now the IAEA is ready to speak about thyroid cancers, but what about the increase of other illnesses and sicknesses ? for instance diseases of the respiratory system and others ? The NGO's should not wait 20 years for the professionals of the IAEA to recognise those diseases. 10 years ago, it would have been crucial to help the children. Our task today is to look ourselves for ways to help them. Otherwise, we could well have to wait for another 50 years.

We are actually monitoring, from the first of September to the first of June of the following year, the health of the children we have sent abroad. We have managed to send about 80,000 children from contaminated areas to several foreign countries, for 6 and 10 weeks for recuperation. The document we just published on this monitoring, had the effect of a cold shower for the government, and it was very inspiring for our organisation.

272 of the children who went to the UK for 6 weeks, were monitored as to their absence from school from September to June. They missed school 3.5 times less often than the control group, who had not left Belarus.

The Canadian government monitored the level of Cesium 137 in 3,137 children at their arrival. When they departed, 6 weeks later, they had 2.5 times less Cesium 137 in their bodies.

I think that without international co-operation, it's impossible to find solutions to all these problems in Belarus, Russia and Ukraine. For us, borders do not exist anymore, there are children, they are the Children of Chernobyl.

The President :

Thank you very much, Dr. Pankratz.

Now I give the floor to Professor Galina Drozdova.

Prof. Galina A. Drozdova :

Ten years have passed since the Chernobyl accident, the worst catastrophe experienced by humanity. It was believed that 10 years would be enough to assess completely this catastrophe, including the medical consequences. Unfortunately 10 years later, there are many more questions than answers. One of the reasons for this is that it is almost impossible to find reliable and objective information on the long-term medical consequences of this accident.

The first official information, received after 3-4 years, didn't give any causes for concern. The report presented by the State's Medical Biophysics Institute, at the Congress of the Soviet Committee of "International Physicians for the Prevention of Nuclear War (IPPNW)", Moscow, in 1989, declared that there was no risk at all for life outside the 30 km zone, even if the radioactive clouds reached over much larger areas.

I attended this Congress, and I remember the many questions asked to the speakers. The responses given were very detailed, and the speakers tried to prove that statistical data on births and early infant deaths showed no difference between the contaminated and the control zones. This was the first medical report ever. They even gave written data. This report raised heated discussions among the physicians, who did not believe in any official statistics. At this time, we had no other source of information whatsoever. As a consequence, many preventive measures, which could have been taken, were not taken.

At the beginning of the 90's, the physicians who worked in the contaminated areas, realised that the official position of the Ministry of Health had nothing to do with the reality. Unfortunately, the moment to undertake preventive measures had passed.

We have inherited the lack of information from the Soviet system, where lies and denial of the truth were the official policy. It would be naïve to believe that the official way of thinking has changed because of a short period of transparency (Glasnost).

It was only very recently that we learned that some radioactive clouds, drifting in the direction of Moscow, were sprayed and forced to come down as rain by military pilots from Gomel, according to orders given by Moscow. As a result, Belarus and especially the Gomel area received 75% of all radioactive precipitation. This was caused not only by the Chernobyl accident, but by an official decision of the government of the Soviet Union.

10 years have passed, the Soviet Union has collapsed. Now it is clear that it is impossible to solve the problem of decontamination. There is no way, neither in theory nor in practice, to oblige the genie to re-enter the bottle.

Meanwhile, our states and international organisations or foundations have spent funds to alleviate the consequences of the Chernobyl catastrophe. How much money ? Nobody in the world knows... Until now, about 50 different organisations or funds with the name of Chernobyl have been created. Unfortunately, the simple people living in the areas contaminated by the radioactivity receive almost nothing. The vain endeavours to relocate people didn't give the expected results, because the new places were even worse, and people preferred to come back to their old houses.

At present no fund, no state organisations have launched any comprehensive socio-medical program to assess the consequences of Chernobyl. The people who live in polluted areas don't know exactly what dose of radiation is harmless for 1 year, for 10 years or for the whole life. Nobody knows when people should be obliged to change their place of residence, or what is the level of soil pollution which allows people to stay at home and eat their home-grown fruits and vegetables.

The lack of information caused the fear of the unknown. This fear has objective grounds. The medical statistics show that oncological diseases are increasing in children. The examination of school children in Gomel, performed by French doctors, showed that among 1,500 children, only 2% are healthy. 96% of all children in Belarus present various mental disturbances. The specialists of the Gomel Medical Institute found many heart disorders in children, having accumulated high doses in their bodies.

The amount of literature about Chernobyl has grown enormously, but it is very difficult to find objective basic information, which would be very important for comprehensive socio-medical programmes. Recently, secret military documents have been released, and we know precisely the official number of military liquidators, which were irradiated with different doses until November 1996.

Number of military liquidators exposed to radiation from the onset of work until 11 November 1986

	Total number	generals	officers	soldiers
exposed until 11.11.86	66.762	50	8378	58.324
Left the region	48.141	37	5.883	42.221
Dose :				
up to 25 rem	46.076	17	5.195	40.864
25-50 rem	2.041	19	674	1.348
over 50 rem	21	1	14	6
Stayed in Chernobyl	13.018	13	2.495	16.026

Even non professionals can see from this table that the data are not complete, and that it raises many questions. Take for instance the group with less than 25 rem, which is the maximal admissible dose in case of an accident. 24 rem are less than this dose and 5 rem even less. It is incorrect to put in one single group all persons with less than 25 rem, as such limits present a high range of uncertainty.

Moreover, the work at the burst reactor has continued after the 11 of November. What were the doses received by the other military liquidators ? Besides the soldiers, many civilians worked as liquidators in Chernobyl and were exposed to radiation. To what levels ? There exists no information on this.

Different scientists and scientific schools have often very opposite views on the medical consequences of the Chernobyl accident, and the good solutions for the medico-social problems.

As before, the official statistical data continue to differ from the data published by independent experts, and does not correspond to any real medical experience in the polluted areas. Let us, for instance, look at a recent publication on Chernobyl, the first scientific book written by one of the medical governmental officials, already in charge at the time of the catastrophe : "Reality and Myths on Chernobyl"[2]. In this book we can find some official documents and statistical data from the Ministry of Health and the Statistical Committee of the State.

Let us for instance look at the information concerning the liquidators of the Chernobyl disaster (data from the Statistical Committee of the State Ministry of Health)

	Russia	Ukraine	Belarus
N° of liquidators end 90	112,952	148,598	17,657
death/100,000	454	360	249
death/100,000 control group, men 20 to 49 years	506	449	431

This table shows that the death rate among liquidators is lower than in the control group. According to these figures, it has in fact been excellent for your health to take part in the liquidation of the Chernobyl disaster and to be exposed

2 Ilyin, L.A. : "Chernobyl, realities and myths", Moscow (1994), 447 pp.

to radiation. If this is true, one can wonder why all independent states in the former Soviet Union give some social and medical privileges to the liquidators.

In 1993, during the international seminar "Problems of the Alleviation of the Consequences of Chernobyl" in Bryansk, the State Committee for Statistics declared that from 1991 to 1993, there existed no difference in death rates of liquidators and that of the control group (men between 20 and 49 years). One has immediately to call to mind the proverb : "There exist three kinds of lies, and statistics are one of them".

During the past 10 years, the health officials have taken the same stand concerning the morbidity of children who live in contaminated areas. I must draw your attention to the fact that regional health departments, and physicians, are forced to accept the official stand point of the Ministry of Health and to act accordingly.

Things only began to change after the intervention of international experts. As before, there are now approximately 5 million persons who live in polluted villages or rural areas, without knowing their real environmental situation, which creates severe psychological stress.

The fear and the ignorance of the real situation cause troubles including psychological stress. People do not want to have children. In 1994, the birth-rate decreased by more than 30%, compared with the 1985 numbers, and now the birth-rate is : 11/1000. Every second pregnancy ends in an abortion. The combination of all those negative factors provokes a mortality of mothers and children, which is highest in the Gomel area. Meanwhile, the health expenses for Chernobyl have decreased by a factor 11, although new medical problems continue to appear.

Money however is not sufficient to solve the medico-social problems in a satisfactory way. What is needed to build up a complete medical and social programme, to alleviate the consequences of the Chernobyl catastrophe, is comprehensive, objective information on the health of people who live in contaminated areas.

Modern medical science has to answer two main questions : first what kind of disorders are the medical consequences of the Chernobyl disaster, and what kind of disorders will appear in the future ?

The second question is also very important and very controversial : what are the main reasons for these disorders, contamination by consuming polluted food ? other consequences of the disaster ? or a combination of several factors ? or psychological stress as stated by the officials ?

It is very important to establish a life-long follow-up of the health of the children born in areas contaminated by different levels of radiation. This is the only way for a sound medical diagnosis, and for motivated decisions to be taken by future mothers. A stable social development can only take place if the real situation is known, and if a realistic prognosis can be established.

The President :

Thank you Professor Drozdova. Now I give the floor to Professor Larissa Skuratovskaya.

Professor Larissa Skuratovskaya :

I would begin by thanking Dr. Rosalie Bertell, one of the first scientific experts who came to Moscow after Chernobyl, wanting to help us.

10 years after the disaster at the Chernobyl atomic power station (APS), one of the most serious technogenic and humanitarian catastrophes of the 20th century, Russia being a member of the Council of Europe, as well as Ukraine, draws its conclusions. The Russian membership in the Council of Europe means that today, human rights are guaranteed on the whole territory of Russia, in conformity with the European Convention for the Protection of Human Rights and Fundamental Freedoms which was signed in Rome, on November 7, 1950 at governmental level. This Declaration is based on the Universal Declaration of Human Rights, approved by the General Assembly of the United Nations Organisation on December 10, 1948.

It is also very important that today, on the territories of 39 European countries, the respect of human rights is guaranteed to all citizens of the member states of the Council of Europe, and that relations not only between States, High Contracting Parties, but also between citizens and states are regulated by laws, based on high international principles.

The European Convention on Human Rights established the first international guide, based on law system, on the protection of fundamental freedoms. It also contributed to the revision of public laws which are protected by local courts. In those countries, where the provisions of the European Convention are not reflected in national laws, it is extremely difficult for courts to require their execution.

Among the requirements to the States acceeding to the Council of Europe, there is a requirement of provision of conditions in the country, guaranteeing the respect of human rights. Before Russia's admission to the Council of Europe, its Constitution and legislation were exposed to thorough examination. It was pointed out that the Constitution and many laws do correspond to the standards of democratic society. Other laws have still to be improved.

According to the information presented by the All-Russian public association "Chernobyl", the disaster at the Chernobyl APS affected about 3 million persons, who live in more than 1,200 settlements of the Russian Federation (RF).

Just after the disaster, hundreds of thousands citizens of the Soviet Union worked in the area of Chernobyl APS, among them 300,000 from Russia. If not for the courage and self-sacrifice of the participants in the liquidation of the consequences of the catastrophe, its scale could have been immeasurably bigger. In accordance with the data of the association "Chernobyl", more than 32,000 "liquidators" became invalids (average age 35-45 years old), about 8,000 died. During recent years, the level of mortality among the liquidators of 1986 has grown considerably (12.2), and exceeded the control level (11.8). This fact justifies their classification into a group of high risk.

The number of invalids has increased sharply among the liquidators in the last four years. In 1994 for instance, their index of general disability reached 135.4 of each 1,000 liquidators. This means that 13 in 100 liquidators are disabled, which is more than thrice as much as the control index.

The number of thyroid gland cancers has grown among liquidators. The number of diseases of the endocrine system in comparison with the all Russian index, is ten times higher; mental illnesses are 5 times higher; diseases of the digestive and circulatory systems are 3-4 times higher. In 1995 the number and gravity of depressive symptoms has grown thrice, which testifies to the high suicide risk.

Thus, after the Chernobyl disaster a new minority group of people appeared, who need special laws : laws for invalids, for refugees, laws which are usually worked out in extreme situations. Up to 1991, there were no such protective laws.

The first attempt for a legal assessment of the Chernobyl events has been an investigation opened by the Public Prosecutor. It was a criminal investigation, on authority abuses and the non-fulfillment of their responsibilities by officials of ministries and other bodies responsible for the liquidation of the Chernobyl catastrophe. There has also been a special criminal investigation on errors in the construction in the nuclear reactor.

In 1993, taking into account the fact that the disaster took place in Ukraine, and that the victims were in republics of the former Soviet Union, the Office of the Public Prosecutor took the decision to transfer a part of the collected materials to Ukraine and Belarus for further investigation. There the case has not been examined for three years, and now it has actually been dropped.

During the period of democratic reforms in Russia in 1991, a law was adopted : "On the social protection of the citizens affected by radiation as a consequence of the catastrophe at the Chernobyl APS", N° 179 RF. This law which was completed in 1992, and adopted again in November 1995, does not apply directly as well as its earlier version. More than 100 normative and legal acts were created, rendering the fulfillment of the Law even more difficult.

Articles 2 and 3 of Chapter 7 of the new Law of November 24, 1995 state :

"2. The President and the Government of the RF should bring their legal acts into conformity with the Federal Law within three months.

3. The Law enters in force from the date of its publication".

This means that the payment of the pensions for disability, as a result of injuries or professional diseases connected with the Chernobyl catastrophe, should enter into force on November 30, 1995. However, according to the letter N° 381/1-34, of Ms. P. Y. Kashenskaya, Deputy-Minister of Social Protection of Russia, dated January 30, 1996, pensions are to be paid starting from March 2, 1996. This represents a violation of the rights of many citizens.

There are other clauses in this Law, which deteriorate the situation of the rights of those who should be protected by it :

- It provides only for one improvement of the housing conditions
- It only covers transport costs to the place of treatment on the territory of Russia
- It covers dental-care expenditures, excluding metal or ceramic amalgams, which formerly were also paid by the State
- a part of population, living on territories exposed to radiation levels inferior to 5 Curie/square km has been deprived of any protection. Only in the Bryansk region, 352,640 persons, including 89,630 children are concerned.

All these fact contradict Article 55(2) of the Constitution of the Russian Federation (RF), stating that in Russia, no law should be adopted, which denies or derogates any rights or freedoms of individual citizens.

Charging legislative and executive bodies of the local authorities with the control of the application of this Law, is a violation of Article 10 of the Constitution of the RF (the principle of the division of power).

The Constitution of the Russian Federation is the highest juridical force (Art. 15(1)), it should be applied directly and throughout the territory of the RF. About 60 contradictions of the Constitution were found in this law. President Yeltsin asked Mr. V. A. Tumanov, Chairman of the Constitutional Court of the RF, to enquire. But there is no response for the time being.

The activities of groups of citizens in the field of medical care and social security, as indicated in the Law, are carried out in conformity with the Single Federal Program on the Protection of the Population of the Russian Federation from the negative consequences of the catastrophe, from 1992 - 1995 and until 2000. Looking at this program, we see that it has been reduced. From 1992 - 1995, only 24,2 % of the funds have been allocated, including for social security.

An important civil right is the right to information (Art. 29). It is well-known that during the years since the end of the "Cold War", the threatening potentiality of nuclear energy has not decreased. But the transparency and the responsibility of public administrations in this field are still insufficient. The citizens still have no right to participate in the decisions on which our lives depend so much.

The Constitution regulates in general the reasons and the limits of the restriction of citizens rights, including the right to freedom of expression and to access to information (Art. 55 (2),(3).

The list of the subjects where access to information is restricted, is stipulated in the Law "On State Secrets" (Art. 7) and in the Law "On Information, Computerisation, and the Protection of Information" (Art. 10).

The relations with State secrets are regulated by the Law of the RF "On State Secrets" and several acts, issued on the basis of this Law. Article 5 of the Law, stipulates the list of information which can be referred to State Secrets. There are four main domains :

1. Information in the military field,
2. Information in the field of economy, science and technology,
3. Information in the field of foreign policy and economical espionage which may cause damage,
4. Information in the field of intelligence, counter-espionage and operative intelligence activities.

As indicated by the "1995 Report of the Presidential Committee on Human Rights", the list of data which can be classified as secret is wide enough and not defined exhaustively. Art. 2 of the Law stipulates that information can be classified if its divulgation could damage the security of the FR. Articles 1 and 3 of the law of the RF "On Security", contain definitions of the "security" and of the "threats to security."

However, those definitions leave open the possibility of different interpretations. Some information has the status of "Secret 1" according to the Law. In other cases, the decisions to restrict the access to information are taken by State officials. The President or the RF has the right to nominate those officials. The list has been published in the Presidential Instruction of 11 February, 1994. Actually, 42 officials have the right to classify information as secret, and to restrict citizens' access to it at free will. Article 29 (4) of the Constitution of the FR stipulates that the list of data covered by State Secret must be defined by Federal Law. However this list was fixed by a Decree of the President of the RF, N° 1203 dated November 3, 1995. The opinion of the Presidential Commission on Human Rights is that this list of data, classified by the presidential decree as secret, is groundlessly wide, and that it restricts the constitutional rights of the citizens of access to information.

Thus, we can see that the laws and resolution issued by the government are far from being perfect. This is why it is necessary to discuss widely the drafts of the laws before their adoption, and not to approve them under the pressure of current circumstances (as was the case with the Law N°17).

One of the obligations accepted by Russia as a condition of its accession to the Council of Europe is the renouncement of the death penalty. The Russian authorities have signed a written commitment, promising to carry out an examination of the matter in order to ratify Protocol No. 6 (on the Abolition of the Death Penalty). In accordance with the Constitution, Art. 20, "pending its abolition, capital punishment may be enforced by the federal law as an exceptional punishment for especially grave crimes against life, and the accused should be granted the right to have his case considered by a court of jury." The Criminal Code of the RF however, foresees death penalty for some other crimes. A person convicted to death penalty has the right to appeal to the Court of Appeal, and also to address a request to the President of Russia to obtain mercy (Art. 89 of the Constitution).

According to the report of the organisation " Amnesty International " (September 1993), the capital punishment is foreseen for 14 different categories of crimes. In the report of the General Assembly on the conformity of the legal order of the RF with the standards of the Council of Europe (October 7, 1994), several recommendations were given to courts in order to prevent them to pass capital death penalty sentences in cases which are not foreseen in the Constitution.

From the moment of the accession of the RF to the Council of Europe, execution of death penalties should be reprieved. It causes concern that at press conferences, when questions about the abolition of death penalty in Russia were asked, Mr. V. Lukin, Head of the Russian delegation (January 25

1996), and Mr. E. Primakov, (February 28 1996) answered that "the Russian people are not ready for the abolition of death penalty." As far as I know, no sociological studies were carried out to support such affirmations. In any case, this matter deserves attention, and should be discussed, especially when taking into consideration the possibility of mistakes, as a result of imperfect legal and juridical systems. The public opinion should have the right to know in which cases the courts passed capital sentences, and which of these sentences were executed.

I decided to tackle this matter when the public became alarmed by the arrest of Mr. A. Nikitin, member of the Norwegian ecological organisation "Bellona Foundation", which took place on February 6, 1996. He was charged with espionage against the Russian State, under Article 64 of the Constitution of the Russian Federation, and with revelations of secret data about nuclear burial places in the North. The maximum penalty for this offence is death. The European Parliament adopted a urgent resolution, addressed to the Government of Russia (February 14, 1996). After Yeltsin's visit to Norway, the situation has slightly changed, but the public does not have free access to data on the charges, because this information is restricted.

In 1989, the IAEA established an International Commission to assess the scale and the true consequences of the Chernobyl catastrophe. The summary of the report published by the Commission was : "No danger", because it had used only official data from the Soviet government.

In 1988 a secret directive was issued for Russian physicians, which forbade any activity to find or to establish any implications between the diseases and the radiation. IAEA knew about it and kept mum.

Even in 1992, during the Rio Summit on Ecology, the Head of the Belarussian Delegation informed the world community: "Until now, we have no full available data concerning the tragic consequences of Chernobyl", due to the IAEA position, which protects corporate interests. This organisation was unable to ensure the ecological safety of nuclear power stations, and to prevent the drain of peaceful technology into military weapons. Due to poor activity or indifference, the IAEA played a harmful role in spreading bad, unsafe nuclear technology, all over the world.

In conclusion, I would like to summarise the thoughts and

feelings of all the participants to this Tribunal. Certainly, we can share many important scientific, medical, ecological data around Chernobyl.

However the practical question : "What can we do for Chernobyl ?" should be at the heart of our Tribunal.

How can we talk about the human rights of the Chernobyl victims, when the government stops financing relief programs, leaving suffering people without elementary help ? How can we can reach our goals ?

My proposal is that the Tribunal should prepare a Verdict about the most serious violations of human rights of the victims and suffering people, and address this Verdict to the Presidents of Russia, Ukraine and Belarus, as well as to the State Duma and Governments of these countries, to the Council of Europe, and to the European Union. It is also important to publish the Verdict in the mass media, to attract the attention towards the human rights of this rather big population. We have to struggle for the "Human Rights for the Chernobyl Victims". They have the right to survive !

I give to the Tribunal a document written in Russian by the chief of the liquidators : "Lessons from the Chernobyl catastrophe". I want also to give you the Russian version of the book of Alla Yaroshinskaya : "Chernobyl, secret documents".

The President :

Thank you very much, Professor Skuratovskaya. Thank you also for your documents in Russian. They will be very useful for the Lelio Basso Foundation.

Now we will listen to the comments from our experts : Professor Peter Weish, Vienna and Professor Hari Sharma from Waterloo, Canada.

Professor Hari Sharma :

Members of the Tribunal, Ladies and Gentleman, I am a nuclear chemist, a member of the International Medical Council of Chernobyl. I have worked in the nuclear industry in one way or the other, first as a radio-chemist in the atomic energy establishments for 20 years. I worked with nuclear reactors, and I know that nuclear reactors produce fission products and other radioactive elements, which do emit ionising radiation.

Ionising radiation either destroy totally the cells or destroy them only partially. It is the latter part which is insidious. If a cell is destroyed, no harm is done as we have a redundancy of cells. If the cell is only partially destroyed, then it causes morbidity and mortality.

Having said that, I will go more deeply into the history of nuclear radiation. Since nuclear technology came into being, there have been accidents of all sorts. Dr. Pankratz said that in Canada they have leaks of radioactive water from reactors, yes, they leak contaminated water.

In 1952, a catastrophic accident happened in Canada, the first meltdown of a reactor's core. it was a small reactor compared with today's nuclear reactors, 40 MW. It took about 18 months to clean up the reactor. It seems that not that much activity escaped into the environment, but some did.

Every time such accidents occurred, they have increased the level of radioactivity in the environment. As a result, we are increasingly exposed to ionising radiation.

People don't talk too much these days of the accident which happened in the UK, at Windscale, where there was a meltdown of the reactor's core, causing the release of radioactivity in the environment. Some papers still discuss an increased morbidity among children with thyroid cancers. This accident happened forty years ago, and we are still seeing its consequences. Such consequences are very long-ranged, and they have to be monitored over a long period of time.

The Chernobyl accident represents a quantum jump in the escape of lethal radioactivity into the environment. Such was my opinion, even 10 years ago, and I was of the opinion that the radiation dose should have been monitored for the whole population living nearby. Millions of Curie of Cesium 137 were released into the atmosphere. Dr. Bertell brought all sorts of tissues to me to analyse. That is how I got into the picture. At one time, I had a very large amount of human tissues for analysis, and I believe that it is necessary to monitor those exactly. She brought also plants and some mushrooms, which contained something like 100,000 Becquerels per kilogram of weight. There was a very high accumulation of radioactive Cesium and other isotopes.

Coming back to the functioning of reactors, a colleague of mine, a fellow chemist, was of the opinion that we must fight the ills of technology with technology. Yes, there are accidents in nuclear reactors, nobody can say that there are no accidents. Before coming out here, I looked in a computer how many books there are in our University's library on Chernobyl. There were 40 books. Each one of them stated quite distinctly that it could happen again, because of the defect of the RMBK reactor types.

From my point of view, anything can happen anywhere. Every technology has its risks. If you take a car which may be a Rolls Royce, yet the brakes may fail, some little part can go wrong, and that goes for reactors as well. On the other hand, we do have ways of counteracting those risks, designs can be improved, we can reduce the probability of accidents. If we pay the price, we may get reactors with very small risks.

Having said that, and coming back to the human-rights question, one of the very oldest principles with regard to radiation is the ALARA principle, that is "As Low As Reasonable Achievable". That principle should be the cornerstone of the human rights. During all stages of any nuclear activity, people must be guaranteed that the ALARA principle has been respected, that means that they have been exposed to as low as reasonably achievable radiation.

If we do follow that, and if we do take the public into confidence, I think that we will respect the human rights perspective. That is the most important aspect, whether it concerns nuclear waste or the siting of nuclear reactors or reprocessing facilities. In all these endeavours, I think that the public should be consulted and it must be seen that human rights are respected.

The President :

Thank you very much, Professor Sharma.

I now give the floor to Professor Weish.

Professor Peter Weish :

Honourable Judges, Ladies and Gentlemen, I must apologise, I'm not a specialist in human rights. I'm familiar with the nuclear issue and related issues since more than 25 years, when I worked in a nuclear research center in the field of radiological protection. Afterwards, I spent much time with questions of energy conservation and energy strategies, against the risks of nuclear power and other risks.

I would like to come back to some questions that we discussed this morning, and to comment on a remark made by my friend Wolfgang Kromp, who said that we should not accuse persons for their responsibility in this catastrophe.

I would like to object to this view. On the one hand, he is right when he says that we should not blame people, feeling that everything would have gone well if they would not have done these errors.

But we see that many people in our industrialised world are slaves of the system. We should however not excuse them, they should not be afraid to take their responsibility. Everyone should take their part of responsibility, nobody can be excused not to take their responsibility.

Besides that, the system obliges in many ways people to act like criminals. One very hard lesson we learned long after the Chernobyl catastrophe, was that nothing has changed in our countries, in spite of the fact that a majority of the people turned against nuclear power, having realised the scale of the catastrophe, and that all promises of safety were lies without any ground. In spite of a majority favouring the phasing out of nuclear power, nothing happened really, only very small, tiny changes.

It was very important to find out and to learn that those who have vested interests in the nuclear-military-industrialised-bureaucratised complex, represent a strong dynamic of institutionalised power. It is a very hard task to organise a responsible public opinion in front of this huge complex.

This has not only to do with nuclear power. Big companies, strong vested interests are pushing the technological developments. I feel that it is very important to create a kind of transparency, to stress the responsibility of every individual, and to let people understand that their responsibility is proportional to their knowledge of the situation.

Let me say a few words about the problem of science. We know that reality is a product of information. Many of us, who experienced the nuclear people in their own meetings, feel that they are creating their own reality. We have to counteract this, and to underline the responsibility of these people.

Another short remark on the question of the risk of nuclear facilities. It is true that when you focus on the many special reactor types, you will find many differences. It is therefore very easy to say that Three Mile Island is of no relevance to Chernobyl, this is another reactor type and we have much better reactors.

I remember a discussion when Wolfgang Kromp and I went to Germany after the Three Mile Island accident. Some nuclear engineer said that it was of no relevance, because a nuclear reactor of the Three Mile Island type would never have any chance to be licensed in Germany. That was a very impressive statement.

Wolfgang Kromp said : "Oh, but you must also take into consideration that German reactors would have no chance to be licensed in the United States". Yes, there exist some small differences between reactor types.

When the governor of Pennsylvania visited the USSR after the Three Mile Island accident, the Soviet specialists said : "Three Mile Island is of no relevance for our nuclear industry, because we have better reactors, such an accident could never happen in the Soviet-Union".

It is therefore very important to look not at the differences, but at the common features. Every reactor, whatever its type, is producing energy from very poisonous materials, concentrated in a very complex system, with many unknown factors.

This is the main feature of modern industry, and not only of the nuclear industry. They are criminal industrial systems, which have no possibility to function in a moral way. Manfred Hinze, a German professor, said many years ago : "Our industry is interested in profit. To expect moral considerations from the industry, is as hopeless as the chance to see a machine smile."

Therefore, we have to stress the responsibility of individuals. Human rights should not be violated. One basic human right is to be able to influence the environment in which you are living. Another is to be able to act in a responsible ethical way. Thus, to be enslaved by institutions, represents a violation of human rights.

Finally, I would like to stress the fact that human rights should also be balanced by human obligations. This is often forgotten. We are all very sensitive to our human rights violations, but we must not forget to act in a responsible way. This obligation applies to everyone, at every level of responsibility.

Scientists in particular, have to liberate themselves from a system which reduces them to mere tools in the hands of industry.

The President :

Thanks very much to our two experts.

I would like to open a discussion on human rights.

I see that Dr. Kromp has returned and if he wishes to comment to Professor Weish, I will give him the floor.

Regarding human rights, we have to look at different aspects and I would like to hear the experts on this.

Dr. Rosalie Bertell :

I think that it is important to consider the context, within which an individual makes a bad judgement, that can be recognised retrospectively. Certain facts in the Chernobyl accident clearly stand out.

One is the May 1 celebration in Kiev, where the people were not informed about the fallout. Little children went out to celebrate May Day and participated in the Parade, wearing summer dresses with their arms bared and they were seriously exposed. There is a clear responsibility there, for withholding the truth.

This happened however in a society that accepted that kind of lies at all levels. I remember that after the Korean war, a US military pilot said in public, at a conference, that it was acceptable for military people to drop atomic bombs in World War II, but no more so in the Korean, or the Vietnam war. At the end of World War 2, the popular support was extreme, horrible. The enemy had been "demonised" to such a point, that there was no criticism whatsoever left among the people, and that the armed forces thought that they

70

were allowed, even encouraged to do such horrible things. This was no longer the case later on.

As individuals, we forget our responsibility towards this general attitude. We forget to speak out, and to stand against human rights violations on all levels. This happened even in 1995 in the United States. For the 50th commemoration of Hiroshima and Nagasaki, the United States government commissioned a historical report, to be put in the Smithsonian Institute, and the veterans objected to it, arguing that it was against their memory of WW II. The government and the Smithsonian Institute failed to put the exhibit out, even though it was the best documented historical record.

So every one of us is responsible. We do have to hold the individual responsible, but we have to recognise our own responsibility in allowing such a society and a milieu to develop, where these kinds of violence can occur.

The President :

Dr. Bertell discussed one aspect of the problem of responsibility as regard to human rights. One other aspect is the question of liability, and the other face of this particular coin is the right to justice, it has to do with impunity. Can we oblige people who were responsible for terrible consequences to be liable ?

Another aspect is the question of the reparation for the victims, which is an independent problem, because of course the responsible persons cannot pay for the consequences. A person who has made a great error in the running of a nuclear plant, is unable to pay for the consequences, so there is a need for another solution.

My third remark is that the question of responsibility is linked to the concept of causality. It is very difficult to identify the causes for an accident. We heard for instance this morning that there still are some disagreements about the causes of Chernobyl, whether it was inherent to the reactor, or due to some external factor. It remains difficult, even for scientists, to determine the causality, a causality which is, of course, necessary to make someone responsible for the consequences.

Professor Weish :

I would like to remind that generally there are three conditions determining responsibility :

1. A causal relationship must exist
2. This relationship must be known to those who act
3. Alternatives must exist.

On all these levels, the nuclear people try to escape the rules. They refuse to admit that low-level radiation have any effects. In Austria, they declare that there are no alternatives to nuclear power. This allows them to reject any responsibility.

It is very hard to blame people from the nuclear complex for not accepting alternatives, because they are enslaved by the system.

But I feel there exists a close relationship between the responsibility of those who cause damage, and the compensation for the victims : if those who are responsible would acknowledge their responsibility, it would be very clear that they should also compensate. This is why they refuse to admit their guilt, and why the victims are not compensated.

A basic human feature is to hide things in the first instance. Every small child, if it breaks something expensive, tries to hide the fragments, as not to be blamed for this. This principle can be found on all levels. At each level, everyone wants to restrict the information and to play down the whole event, this is a fundamental human principle.

Professor Hari Sharma :

Chernobyl illustrated quite clearly that it is impossible to hide such accidents. In Sweden, where the accident was discovered, the exposure could be gauged. It is also known that 2% of the activity came down within a 30 kilometre radius of the reactor itself, 50% went across the boundary of the former Soviet Union. In 1986, the Conferences of Vienna and then Paris labelled clearly the liability on the operators of the facility.

When a Russian space-ship fell in Alberta, the Canadian government presented a claim, declaring that it cost them 4 million dollars, and they got this money from Russia. So it is possible to solve material aspect of claims.

Regarding Chernobyl as reparations are concerned, human health, malignancies of any kind are not mentioned, and I think that this should be incorporated. Radiation injuries can be quantified, it has been done in some cases in the United States, by analysing the radiation and finding out the dose. There exists a scale of risks, maybe not perfect, with risks proportional to the amount of dose received.

In the Chernobyl accident, the people suffering from an acute radiation syndrome (ARS), have died, the mortality was almost 100 percent. The effect of smaller doses is more difficult to assess. We can adopt a linear hypothesis and quantify the damage, and then fix the rate of compensation in money. You pay, like a person who kills someone with her car, it is now considered to amount to 10 million dollars. But all these figures do not take into account the morbidity and the future mortality. I think the Tribunal should look into this and make recommendations.

The President :

Thank you very much.

Judge Surendar Gadekar :

It seems to me that in the ALARA principle, the word "Reasonable" is the most controversial word. For instance, the ex-chairman of the Indian Atomic Committee declared that for a poor country like India, it was unreasonable to spend so much on safety. He said that we should reduce the money spent on safety, this would be safe enough for India.

What is reasonable is linked on one side to the health of the people, and on the other side represents money from some other people. Those who are going to pay this money, feel that the amount that is spent is unreasonable. I would like your comments on that.

Professor Hari Sharma :

Well, I did expect a question on what is reasonable and what is unreasonable.

I can tell you a very simple way how it comes to that kind of justification. We can reduce the level of radiation by putting up shields around the reactor, or devices capturing the radioactive isotopes. In my Institute I look into the aspect of risk and benefits. If you take account of costs, of the risks and benefits to be awaited, there is a cost point where you draw the line.

As far as reasonable and unreasonable are concerned, I think that is a good point. What becomes unreasonable here, is probably reasonable elsewhere, depending on the cost and the benefits of the operations.

When I commented about fighting the use of technology with technology, the example was given that cars are causing excessive pollution, but would we go back to horse buggies ? Of course everyone would refuse because we would have pollution from the droppings. It is a very difficult question to tackle, and we need answers to that question.

I thought that the Chernobyl accident provided quite a good opportunity to find out the facts of radiation effects upon populations. It is a terrible tragedy that it happened, but we could get many answers about morbidity and mortality, about human health damages caused by such accidents, and from that, we could learn what is reasonable and what is unreasonable.

The President :

I will allow all questions now, and the answers will be given afterwards.

Judge Surendar Gadekar :

The costs of human life are put differently in different parts of the worlds. When you talk about compensation for morbidity, it would depend upon where that accident happened, and again that is a judgement which is made by the people who have to pay, its not a judge's opinion.

Judge Corinne Kumar :

With all that we have heard this morning, what does the fundamental right to life mean today? Have the concepts and categories that we use become insufficient to meet the violence against the children of Rongelap, the children of Chernobyl ?

I put this questions to the two Russian Professors, Galina and Larissa : what does the fundamental right to life mean, when mothers, in Micronesia and Polynesia, deliver masses of flesh called "jelly-babies" ? What answer can we give to that ?

74

My second comment and question goes into the area of the human rights discourse. What history, ideology, philosophy informs the international human rights discourse, the Universal Declaration of Human Rights ?

I address this comment and my question to one of the speakers, who talked in terms of the victim being revictimised. When we use the dominant human rights discourse, and the existing international instruments of humanitarian law, which we have to use, then we allow ourselves to be trapped into the chains of the nation state. There exists no mechanism by which individuals can seek compensation from the violence exerted on them by national state. Nuclear energy is indeed a project of the nation states. Where do you take nation states for their repression against the people?

Friends, listening today, I also feel that if we begin to explore, and we must begin to explore, another terrain, a new generation of human rights, this cannot come from the side of the nuclear establishment, it cannot come from those who tell us about safe places and permissible levels of radiation. But it will come from people who have stayed outside the system of power and privilege. When I try to see through the eyes of the victims, which is what the Permanent People's Tribunal tries to do, and Tribunals like this do all over the world, to break the kinds of silence surrounding the victims, the victims begin to find a new voice through the language of suffering. The language of suffering confronts the language of expertise. It is important to strengthen their voices, and to seek another kind of human rights terrain and discourse, another way of understanding this new alternative, because I think that people are moved by the stories of the victims.

Judge Mitsuo Okamoto :

I have three short questions. The first one : I wonder if you can speak of nuclear technology ? If a mistake during operations of a nuclear installation causes such accidents, can it still be called technology ? You talked about reducing the accidents, reducing the danger to as low as possible, but I question if you can ever reduce nuclear technology to such an extent that humanity can tolerate ?

My second question is to Professor Weish : you were saying that we can distinguish the people from the system, that we cannot blame people, but must question the system. Is this really possible with the very complicated and dangerous systems we have today ?

Concerning human rights, we have observed in Hiroshima and Nagasaki that the victims of the bombing have remained silent for many years, because they were afraid of being discriminated against. There existed real discrimination against the survivors, because people are still afraid that, if they marry a survivor, their children or children's children may present a malignancy which is intrinsic to the radiation disease. Although I haven't visited the irradiated area in the former Soviet Union, I have a suspicion that people living in the irradiated areas, even if at the moment they may not have any symptoms, yet experience tremendous psychological pressure, afraid that they might be discriminated against, for the same reasons as in Hiroshima and Nagasaki. This is the kind of question we have to address in this Tribunal.

Judge Freda Meissner-Blau :

I have three short questions to Dr. Pankratz and Dr. Grushevaya.

1. In the report of its Committee in 1989, the IAEA claimed that the government of Belarus had exaggerated and exceeded the necessity of evacuation. Do you think that the attempts of your government to have people returning into the polluted areas, may be an answer to the 1989 claim of the IAEA ?

2. How would you consider the cross responsibility of your government and of the international community ?

3. What is the experience of your NGOs (in Ukraine as well) ? Is the help you are giving to the Children of Chernobyl being helped or hindered by your government ? For instance, is there a tax deduction for humanitarian aid etc. etc. ? Can you give us a little bit of a picture of the aid's situation and the obstacles to it ?

Dr. Yuri Pankratz :

In 1990 the Republic of Belarus took a very important decision : they adopted a programme for resettlement. We were very thankful to the new parliament who made this decision.

Today our parliament has almost no role, because we have almost a dictatorship with President Lukashenko and his team. There are two main reasons why they decided to give green lights for people to resettle.

The first one is the economic situation. Alla Yaroshinskaya already mentioned it : when we increased the standard admissible dose for milk, we saved 25 million rubles. There is no money in Belarus and there is a crisis. That is why people are living on land which has 1-5 Curie per square kilometre.

The second one is somehow connected with the interests of the IAEA : as far as I understand, these two ideas of giving people the permission to resettle and of encouraging them to do so, were underlined by Lukashenko, 4 days ago at the IAEA Conference, in three paragraphs of his speech, maybe in order to get some money or for another reason.

On the question of the cross responsibility between the national government of Belarus and the international community, Belarus is in a very strange situation, we have never had any nuclear power station. As a consequence, according to the laws, there are no compensations, no special funds have been provisioned. In our Congress, we asked for the establishment of a special international insurance fund, to compensate any nuclear disaster in any country, because every country can be a victim. Sweden was for instance the first country to spread information about Chernobyl. They are also the victims of the Chernobyl disaster, but they have never been compensated by anybody. The same is true for Belarus.

That is why I think that it is the responsibility of the world community, and of the European Union, to install this Special Fund. I don't know what would be the source, maybe from the nuclear power stations, from the profits they make. I think it would be better to have an independent Fund, established for instance by the World Bank as an insurance Fund. People are dependent on those who give the money. This Fund should be independent from the IAEA.

Judge Freda Meissner-Blau :

Can you please explain why you think it should be independent ?

Dr. Yuri Pankratz :

I mean independent from the IAEA, because those who give the money have the saying, and would again dictate their will.

As to your question about the obstacles put on the activity of NGOs, some people in this room have visited our country. The government, it makes no difference whether communist or not, controls everything, since 70 years. I will give you one example which will help you to understand. I visited a region 4 years ago, and a leading official of the communist party wanted to speak to the professor from Minsk. As I was independent, and represented the "Children of Chernobyl", I went. When I entered his room, there were Marx and Lenin on the wall, and I asked him, "Do you have a child ?" and he said that he had two kids. I told him, "I'm very sorry, but your kids will never go to any foreign country for recuperation with our Foundation. "Why? You are an anti-communist !", he said. I said : "You are part of the 2% privileged in our country, you receive a good salary, this has only to do with economical problems". He never understood. He was the tsar in this region, he controlled everything, and suddenly a professor from Minsk arrives and he is no more the tsar.

The problem is that the government doesn't want to loose control, this is very difficult to understand for people with a western mentality.

Although we are a very important organisation, we have never received one ruble, one dollar from our government ! Never ! Sometimes they want to make national heroes of us, give us medals, although we cost them not a single ruble. At the same time, they decide to control everything, they give us no freedom whatsoever. If you give some freedom to the people, they might take decisions, take further steps and then if the government suddenly takes a very important decision, the people might decide that they don't need it.

This is a very paradoxical situation. I think that all over the world there is a tendency where the non-governmental movement is increasing at a somewhat different pace, the red tape being in Canada or in the United States. That is why the obstacles made by the government are artificial obstacles.

Another example and I will finish. Take a family in Belarus, and a family in Germany, or Canada or the United States, who wants to invite a kid into their the country. There is a fund, a charitable non-governmental organisation, we help them to make all the papers and to organise this visit.

However there is another level : the Minister of Education keeps the right to give permission to send the kids. Every one of the 80,000 children who are sent to other countries, needs to get this permission from the Minister of Education of our country and from our local authorities. They keep this key, and that is why we feel frustrated. We don't want to fight with the government, but they make such obstacles. We try to make people all over the world realise that non-governmental organisations are being controlled by our government in this way.

The President :

Thank you very much. Now we can continue.

Dr. Rosalie Bertell :

I just want to respond to Judge Meissner-Blau's question, on whether or not the IAEA is behind moving the people back in Belarus.

In the 1990 meeting of the ICRP, the principle of ALARA was being used against the nuclear industry, saying that they had to improve the conditions of the Chernobyl victims, and that their exposure should be made as low as reasonably achievable. This meant evacuate them, and get the contamination out of the food supply, as fast as possible.

What happened was, that 4 years after the catastrophe, the ICRP stated that "ALARA does not apply to an accidental situation".

They elaborated a completely new philosophy : in an accidental situation, the *status quo* is that the people are exposed and contaminated. According to the new principle, you have therefore to justify every reduction in exposure, you have to prove that the amount of money you pay to reduce exposure, gives a corresponding increase in good health. They totally turned upside down the meaning of ALARA, which was then fed into the IAEA, and by the IAEA into all the national governmental nuclear agencies.

I do believe that the Chernobyl victims have been held hostage by this new philosophy. We know that the reactor is still open on two sides, it is still leaking and there still is great need for international help to cope with the reactor itself. If the governments of Belarus, Ukraine and Russia do not apply the revised ALARA definition, they will get no international help in terms of money and nuclear experts, to help them to cope with this continuing accident and disaster.

The President :

Thank you very much, Dr. Bertell.

Professor Peter Weish :

I would like to answer the question of whether it is possible to separate people from the system. Yes and no, it must be possible. We should create more sensitivity and awareness of the fact that people tend to be slaves of the system. We should stress also the need for them to act in a responsible way.

Everyone has some freedom in his actions, and therefore no excuse for an irresponsible behaviour. We must try to have an open discussion, beyond the borders of a specific situation, to address the IAEA and to discuss with those people personally, outside their respective organisations, to stress their personal responsibility.

What is "reasonable"? If health is balanced against money, it should also be taken into account that personal money and the health of others don't balance too well. But I feel that if we look in a rational way at these problems, we should also take into account another, much vaster horizon.

As an ecologist, I look far back to the origins of human beings, and I also try to look ahead to the future. We have to assess technologies, as to whether they help sustainable development, or play against it.

I feel that nuclear power is a prime example of a technology which does not fit into a sustainable development. It is an obstacle to sustainable development. The greatest danger is that it forecloses other energy strategies, when it is so urgent to search for sustainable alternatives, in the energy field, as in others, and in the whole society.

The President :

I thank you very much, Professor Weish.

Professor Hari Sharma :

The question of the cost of human life is difficult to answer. I went back to India only a few months ago, after an absence of 2O years, and the cost of life has changed considerable over that period. If you compare it to the cost of life in the United States or Canada, it is probably less than one tenth. It's hard to answer these questions. It's to lawyers to answer them. In the reparations lawsuits, they are accustomed to such questions.

As to human rights, in the 30's in India, there were no human rights, there were no elections, there was British rule, and we were obeying them, and under those conditions, there were no human rights for us. The same was true at the time of the Chernobyl catastrophe : there were no elections, people were unaware of their rights.

Now I live in Canada, where we have the obligation to assess human rights violations. Energy production increases life expectancy, there exists a linear relationship. We had a symposium just after the Chernobyl accident, and we had lots of discussions over one week. It was very clear that in countries where the *per capita* use of energy was low, the life expectancy was low. There exists such a relationship, you may challenge it, but it is there, and these are the societal obligations we have towards other nations.

People who live close to nuclear reactors which release radioactivity, are exposed to radiation. This is where the human rights come in.

Dr. Wolfgang Kromp :

It was not my intention to deny the responsibility of those who work in the nuclear energy sector. I only wanted to draw your attention on the fact that you should be careful when blaming individuals. I wanted much more to draw your attention on the system, standing behind those individuals. These workers are like Martians and once you remove them, others will come.

We have to confront the whole system, a system which might be the cause of the irresponsible behaviour of the population. We have to go to the roots, and we should not forget to take care of those people which are the victims of this cruel system.

The President :

Thank you very much.

I now call Dr. Sergii Mirnyi.

Dr. Sergii Mirnyi :

I want also to comment on human rights, and convey facts about some actions I witnessed, which can be classified, according to international law, as experimentation on people.

In our regiment of liquidators, we were told that these people were to be exposed each day to 2 rem maximum. According to the instructions we were given, the liquidators were forced to take 2 rem/day, a dose which was considered to be acceptable, I repeat, considered to be acceptable. The purpose of this undertaking was to expose people, in order to perform biochemical experiments. Before going into the zone, these people had their blood taken for special biochemical tests. After having been exposed to such doses every day, they had to go for more blood tests. The maximum admissible dose at that time in the zone was 25 rem.

These people were not volunteers, they were just ordinary citizens, they were taken from the cities unto the zone, to serve in the army and to work on the liquidation of this accident. As far as I know, such medical experiments on groups of people are not allowed, neither with military, no students, etc.

I have worked on a book on Chernobyl stories, I have written a story before I knew anything of this Tribunal, and I have called it "Statement of Evidence". It reveals the kinds of experiences we were subjected to. I would like to give it to the Tribunal.

The President :

Thank you very much, Dr. Mirnyi.

4. EVIDENCE OF GENETIC OR TERATOGENIC DAMAGE TO THE ENVIRONMENT AND HUMANS

Speakers :   *Ms. Cornelia Hesse-Honegger, scientific illustrator specialising in Zoology,*

Ms. Solange Fernex, former Member of the European Parliament

Dr. Sanghamitra Gadekar, International Medical Commission on Chernobyl

<u>The President :</u>

I now give the floor to Ms. Cornelia Hesse-Honegger.

<u>Ms. Cornelia Hesse-Honegger :</u>

I would like to thank the Tribunal very much for listening to evidence, which officially has no relation whatsoever with nuclear radiation.

We have to look very closely at three types of phenomena in nature : The first is nature as we get it from God, the second is nature that we see through laboratory work, and the third one is the nature that is breaking apart, because of our everyday waste disposals into it.

I am a scientific illustrator, and I have been working for 25 years at the University of Zurich, mostly for geneticists and taxonomists. I will show you slides of my work (fig. 1 - 8).

I have been drawing mutant drosophiles for a geneticist for his studies with the poison EMS. On the left, you see the head of a mutated fly. On the right you see a normal fly.

It is only after many years, that I realised that a similar kind of poison, used as Agent Orange in Vietnam, produced very similar deformities in children. Today, a deformed child is born every day in this area.

While I was working with these drosophiles, I started as a free artist to paint leaf bugs, which are a kind of very small insect, and I painted them because they looked so beautiful.

While I was painting them, there were so many accidents and nuclear tests. I had seen that many of the leaf bugs that I had been painting, became extinct in the area of

Switzerland where I had collected them, and I was very much upset about this fact. I worried about what was happening.

I went to the laboratory, to my professor and asked him : "Please give me mutated lab flies, which I consider as being prototypes of the new nature to come, if we continue to put all these wastes into nature, without control".

You see here a red eye on this fly. The whole shape of the head is deformed. There are parts of a wing which grow out of the eye. The germinal cells of the fly have been irradiated, and the cells cannot decide anymore if they want to become an eye or a wing. This is the result of a laboratory experiment for genetic research.

While I was doing this work, the Chernobyl catastrophe happened. I thought that these areas, where the fallout had come down, resembled what was happening in a laboratory. I went to Sweden, to the region where the highest fallout had been registered, to look if I could find leaf bugs, and see if they showed some deformities in their bodies. The scientists who worked with the drosophiles told me :"It is not worth going to Sweden, because nothing happened there". That was in summer 1987.

I had decided to wait one year to study the second generation of leaf bugs. I found plants with deformities like this clover : instead of pink flowers, it has yellow flowers. These are also leaves that are deformed. Here on the left, you have a normal head of a leaf bug, and on the right you have one with antennas that look like sausages, and a growth out of the eye.

These leaf bugs are very good indicators, because when they come out of their eggs, they are less than one millimetre long, and they have a trunk with which they suck the water out of the leaves. I thought that on contaminated leaves, leaf bugs would have a high body dose of radiation, because of the smallness of the animal. They change also skin about 5 times in their life, during which they are very exposed to external contamination.

This is also the head of a leaf bug, you see the sausage-like antenna. Here on the left side, this is a larva, the left wings are already divided, but different from the right wings.

I went also to the southern part of Switzerland, where they measured a contamination of 24,000 Becquerels per square meter. I found this cicada, where you can see a part of a leg growing out of the middle leg, it's like a small part growing out.

I collected there two pairs of drosophila melanogaster, took them back into my studio, bred them and made them grow. Already in the first generation, I saw terrible mutations, like the splitting of the face, changed size of the eyes, and deformities of the abdomen. Here you have the comparison of a deformed with a normal abdomen. Here is a deformity of the left wing, which looks like a nut.

I published this work in Switzerland, and the scientists were very angry at me, because the drosophile is like a holy cow. It is not to be handled by anyone outside of the academic world. They told me that these kinds of mutations only happen when the drosophiles are irradiated by very high doses. I thought well, everybody knows that nuclear power plants release only very low doses. Everything there would have to be very healthy.

So I went to look around the Swiss nuclear power plants, which are of course the cleanest in the world, and I found horrible deformities of insects. I started to walk in the main wind directions and to search for several different insects. This ear worm has a short leg, uneven wings, its left wing looks like a balloon.

When I published this work, they were even more angry at me. Here you see the pattern on the left side is different than on the right side. When you imagine that this creature is 2 millimetres long, who would care to look at such small animals?

I thought that maybe I am wrong, I have to go to other places to check on these leaf bugs, so I went to Sellafield. Here are two leaf bugs, one has a growth on the antenna, a dark point, here on the right side, the wings are deformed. This is a cicada with a hole in its middle.

I had the possibility to go to Chernobyl in 1990. This is a leaf bug I found in Pripyat, you see that the middle leg on the right side is shorter. In Polesskoye, almost every insect I collected was deformed. Here you see a deformed wing, here the left antenna has a missing segment. Here you can see a deformed larva. This insect has been collected at the border of the 30 km zone. You see a deformed left leg and the general absence of symmetry.

I then went to Three Mile Island, where I found the most heavy and most deformed insects just around the power plant.

I was puzzled by the question how after so many years, one would still see some consequences from the accident. I think I can say that what I found has more to do with the everyday clean-up situation, where sometimes a filter is collapsing, or Tritium is released into the water. I have studied the papers of the clean-up and there is no mention of any study of the insects or other living organisms in the river during all this time, although the largest fish grounds are just a little bit further down, at the border of the sea.

Here is a cicada with a growth out of the eye from Three Mile Island. Here is a leaf bug, collected near the nuclear power plant of Peach Bottom. You can see that the segments of the abdomen are irregular, like those of the drosophile from Tessin.

Last year I went to Krümmel, in the north of Germany, and there I found a kind of growth on the surface of the wings and deformed neck plates in insects.

Many scientists have criticised me, saying that I was only looking at places where something had happened, and not in the nice and clean places. Personally, I don't believe that such places exist, it's like believing in paradise.

However, I started a more comprehensive study in the Canton of Aargau, in Switzerland, where 4 nuclear power plants and one research plant are located. I have collected leaf bugs on every cross-section of the lines of the 1/5,000 map, the same amount of insects or leaf bugs, so that I can compare one place to the other. I have found the worst deformities in the close neighbourhood of the nuclear power plants, and in the wind direction. I have looked at morphological deformities, like uneven wings and length of wings, or uneven neck plates, or feelers. It is interesting that when these insects are split in half, one half is healthy and the other part is deformed.

I would like to tell the Judges that biologists, geneticist, scientists, who are the experts that we, the people, pay every day for their research, don't do research that helps us to understand what is going on with nature.

As I tried to explain to the Tribunal, at the time where I drew those drosophiles, the US army was pouring down these defoliants over Vietnam. During all this time, I heard no cry from scientists, saying, "Are you crazy? This is a mutagenic substance, and you are deforming and mutating the population, and the plant life and animal life for generations".

The same thing happens today with radioactivity. The scientists know perfectly well that radioactive substances are mutagenic. I hear none of them saying : "For heavens sake, we have to find out what's going on !", despite the fact that the curiosity of the researchers should push them to try to understand what is happening.

I think that its important that the Judges also remind the scientists of the responsibility they carry, doing this kind of research and being the experts for the people, to speak out to us, in our language, so that we can understand what is happening.

I thank you.

The President :

I thank you very much, Ms. Hesse-Honegger

I now give the floor to Ms. Solange Fernex.

Ms. Solange Fernex :

I want to show to the Tribunal a document, which was filmed in the region of Chernobyl, by a reporter from the Ukrainian Television, M. Kuznetsov, in early 1990. He visited several hospitals and Research Institutes in Kiev, in Jitomir and inside the evacuated zone of 30 km.

A botanist-geneticist speaks : "We are inside the 30 km zone, surrounding the Chernobyl reactor. On 25 square meters, I have grown small pines in a tree nursery, from seeds collected on an unique tree, inside the zone. Those seedlings are 4 years old. You can see, on this very small surface, each and every one of the 25 mutations known world-wide for this variety of Pinus : gigantism, dwarfism, asymmetrical implantation of needles, of branches, abnormally long or short needles, short plummets, you can discover all this and much more on those little pine trees." (the camera goes around and shows details).

<u>A veterinary speaks</u> : "Our Institute for Veterinary Medicine is situated in the town of Jitomir. After the Chernobyl catastrophe, we noticed a highly increased number of deformities in the state-farms. Pigs were born with two heads, calves with missing limbs, missing hind legs especially, Siamese calves. Some of these deformities were lethal at an early stage of the development of the fetuses, other were born alive and died within a few hours. Here you can see a calf with 3 horns, here a horse which did not survive the first hours".

<u>Physicians speak</u> : "When we looked at microscopic slides of biopsies, taken from liquidators coming from Chernobyl, we saw enormous black dots. We thought that they must be artefacts and we prepared new slides. They were very big radioactive particles, especially Plutonium. We looked at the literature, and the only studies we found were experimental studies performed by German scientists on rabbits, to assess the consequences of injections of Plutonium. Our material comes from liquidators, from human living beings !"

<u>A mid-wife from Jitomir speaks</u> : "Today, women worry when they become pregnant. Pregnancies often have unfavourable outcomes, we observe an important increase in abortions, with often very deformed fetuses. Women are bleeding. Here you see a premature baby. We put him in a breeder. On this screen you can follow his cardiac rhythm : it is very irregular and chaotic. He presents red plaques on his body."

Then follow a long series of pictures of deformed fetuses and stillborn or heavily deformed babies, accompanied by the lamentations of an Orthodox Kyrie ("Pity, oh Lord...").

I want also to present you with some photographs, published by Ms. Adi Roche, who unfortunately could not be present here, as she is in Belarus with relief convoys from her foundation "Children of Chernobyl" (fig 13 - 20). They are quite recent (end of 1995) and have been taken in Minsk. Here you have a child born with multiple deformities of the face, the brain. He died a few months later. Here another child born with anencephalia, which means no brain. He lives as a vegetable, unable to take notice and to respond to any stimulus. His parents have abandoned him. Here you have a child with a severe palatal deformity. After the operation, it had to be fed by tubes, but died soon after. Little Nastia, who is perfectly normal except her deformed legs and clubbed feet, has been successfully operated on in Ireland.

Although early and repeated prenatal examinations are compulsory, and physicians inform the parents about the state of the fetuses, and what to expect, deformed children are born day after day. Their parents often abandon them after a few days, unable to cope with the disaster. Those who survive are treated in the pediatric hospital, until they reach 5 years of age. At this age, they have to move to the pedo-psychiatric ward, where their time of survival is often very short.

I want also to present to you the study undertaken by Dr. Aleksandr Slukvin, working on carp in the Institute for Zoological Genetics (Director : Professor Rosa Gontcharova) in Minsk. Dr. Slukvin is the former head of industrial state fish-farms in Belarus, Russia and Lettonia.

This study was carried in a fish-farm situated 200 km from Minsk. Belarus has 28 such fish-farms, producing carp for the domestic use and for exportation. Fish-farming represents an important economic factor for the country. The physical and chemical parameters (heavy metals, fertilisers and pesticides, radioactivity and oxygen content) of the water and the soil are controlled very carefully, as the economic return of the enterprise depends on it.

The water filling the pond comes from a lake in the neighbourhood, outside the contaminated area and it is practically free of radioactivity (10_{12} Ci). However, since the accident, the muddy bottom of the pond is contaminated with Cs 137. After ploughing the soil of the emptied pond, the radioactivity in the superficial sediment initially declines, but when the pond is filled again with clean, non-radioactive water, the same radioactivity as before is measured on the bottom of the pond. The control pond is situated at 400 km from Chernobyl in a non-radioactive area.

Artificial fecondation is performed with 8 year old parent carp, and the eggs are put in breeders. The development of the eggs, the embryos and the young fish are monitored carefully. Eight year old parent carp lay normally about 2 millions eggs. They have about 800 Bq/kg of Cs 137, which is considered as fully acceptable for consumption. After 6 months, every autumn, the young carp are transferred into deeper winter ponds. Their morphology, size, weight and health is controlled during their transfer. A veterinary doctor is monitoring very carefully diseases and parasites. Before the Chernobyl catastrophe, no serious problems have occurred.

However, since 1988, anomalies were found in the offspring : 70 % of the fertilised eggs do not hatch. The 30 % surviving young fish are put into the summer ponds. After 6 months, 70% of the surviving little carp show macroscopic deformities : the long dorsal fin is missing, deformed of implanted on one side only, the mouth is terribly deformed, one carp was even found with no mouth ! two anal orifices, deformities of the eyes, even absence of eyes, unprotected gills, with missing gill covers. The scales are often abnormal, too small. The pigment on their surface may be missing, such carp seem transparent. The violet-blue mutation, formerly very rare and known in Germany, is now very abundant (fig. 9 -12).

Dr. Slukvin has compared the chromosomes in eyes of 2-3 days old larvae, in the contaminated water and in the control pond : Chromosomal aberrations have doubled, sometimes tripled in the ocular cells. Similar chromosomal aberrations have been noted at the end of the blastula stage of the embryonic development, in the contaminated pond.

Diseases have also increased in carp living in the contaminated pond : inflammations of the swimming bladder, with loss of balance, protozoa, and helminthiasis, viruses etc., probably linked to a reduction of the resistance mechanisms.

Dr. Slukvin and Professor Gontcharova conclude as a result, that carp are very sensitive to radiation. These fishes feed on the 5 upper centimetres of the top-sediment at the bottom of the ponds. As carp possess no stomach to accelerate the digestion, they have very long intestines, filling up all the body cavity.

Those very interesting studies should continue. Unfortunately, Dr. Slukvin has got no support at all for his work, and he has been obliged to discontinue it, having no money for even the gasoline for his small car.

Yesterday, during the IAEA Conference, in the chapter concerning the environment, speakers declared that there are no consequences whatsoever in the water. I took the floor and asked if they were aware of the study by Dr.

Slukvin on the development of carp in fish-farms in Belarus, where 70 % of the eggs do not hatch, and 70 % of the 6 months old little carp present major visible morphological deformities ?

The speaker answered : "It is a very complex problem. Everything depends on the rate of humidity, etc.[3] I was speaking of a fish-farm pond ! It was absolutely ridiculous. The chairman realised the catastrophic impact of this answer. "I do not think that the question has really been answered. Could someone answer this ?". An academician hurried to say that studies were being undertaken, that for the time being, no results had shown any increase of deformities, but that those studies had to carry on. Unfortunately, neither Dr. Slukvin nor Professor Gontcharova had been invited to present their results at the IAEA Conference.

On the day before, the subject had been the health effects. The speaker had stated that there were no genetic effects. He said : "It is impossible to conclude to any modifications of the genetic effects, because there existed no register before the accident".

This was an outright lie. Professor Lazjuk, in Minsk, has a register of deformities which have to be registered, since 1982 (fig. 47), four years before the catastrophe. He noted a significant increase of 4 major deformities in children : i.e. amelia (no or shortened limbs), polydactylia (an excessive number of fingers), anencephaly (no brain), which you can see on the photographs presented by Ms. Adi Roche. Professor Lazjuk has not been invited to comment at the IAEA Conference.

Finally, I would like to read to you an extract of the OCDE report [4] from November 1995, on Chernobyl. This report

---

3 This answer has been deleted in the IAEA report of the iscussion (September 1996, Vienna), whereas they have only printed the second answer to my question.

4 "Chernobyl, 10 years ago. Public Health and radiological Impact". OCDE Paris, November 1995. This report has been written by Dr. Peter Waight (Canada) under the direction of a Drafting Comittee, presided by Dr. Henri Métivier (France), composed of : Dr. H. Métivier (IPSN, France), Dr. P. Jacobi (GSF, Germany), Dr. G. Suskevitch (WHO, Geneva), Dr. H. Brunner (NAZ, Switzerland), Dr. C. Viktorsson (SKI, Sweden), Dr. B. Bennet (UNSCEAR, Vienna), Dr. R. Hance (FAO/IAEA, Vienna), Dr. S. Kumasawa (JAERI, Japan), Dr. S. Kusumi (Japan), Dr. A. Bouville (NCI, USA), Dr. J. Sinnaeve (EU, Brussels), Dr. P. Ilari (OCDE/ARN, Paris) and Dr. E. Lazo (OCDE/AEN, Paris).

has been cited many times during the IAEA conference, especially by Professor Lee from the University of St. Andrews, Scotland, an UNESCO expert, to confirm that radiation was not harmful for health. This report has been written by a team of experts, under the direction of Dr. Henri Métivier, from the French Institute for Radiation Protection and Safety (IPSN).

This report declares, for instance, that : "Very comprehensive medical studies have shown that no anomaly in the field of health can be attributed to the exposure to radiation (...)". Later it states : "In conclusion... the accident of Chernobyl should not be considered as the accident of reference".

The video we have seen, the photographs of deformed children, and the study on carp are only some among many others, which show how cynical such statements are. I believe that they are really criminal. We must refuse that so-called experts continue to deny the evidence, in order to prolonge for some short time the life of a nuclear industry, which is absolutely incompatible with a sustainable future.

The President :

I thank you, Ms. Fernex.

I now give the floor to Dr. Sanghamitra Gadekar.

Dr. Sanghamitra Gadekar :

I will present to the Tribunal our findings on congenital deformities in Rajasthan. The findings are not linked to an accident, but to the day-to-day functioning of a nuclear power plant. These are deformities like those we have already seen in relation to an accidental situation in insects, fish, plants and children of Chernobyl.

Until now, the scientific community has not given enough attention to the fetus. They do not recognise the effects of radiation on the people who are exposed, nor to the next generations. In the past, the effects on the fetus have been researched in animals and humans. Since 1927 and the work of Muller, the genetic and teratogenic effects on the fetus are known.

But nowadays the scientific community tries to push back

this knowledge. They say "that is not important, this has not been observed, such theses cannot be maintained".

We came across this by accident. We were on a survey campaign, and we came across a very small village, where we observed a lot of deformities. We were very puzzled, and decided to study this phenomenon in a scientific way. Thus, we talked to lots of institutions and to experts who could perform scientific investigations on those deformities. But unfortunately, none of them was interested in this kind of study.

After a year of people's pressure, we decided that the civic organisations had to undertake this study themselves. Our experience could maybe help others in similar situations, how to record, how to do surveys and to help themselves.

We launched an appeal across India to many people's organisations, and many ordinary people, scientists, physicians, statisticians became involved. The survey was launched with all their help, and no help whatsoever from the government, completely on a voluntary basis.

We went house to house, door to door, collecting information in 9 villages : 5 villages in the vicinity of the nuclear power plant, and 4 villages situated 40 - 50 kilometres away from it.

For us, the most important information to gather was the experience of the people. The only thing was to translate it in a scientific language. For this, is was necessary to use a scientific method, and to conduct the survey in a proper way.

The first reactor has been functioning for the last 15 years. We recorded all that happened in the last 15 years. As the second came into operation 11 years ago, we surveyed the children under 11 years of age. We recorded all the births and deaths. Pregnancy outcomes were recorded for the last two years.

The total pregnancy outcome was terribly shocking. There were deformities in the general population, and the deformity rate was 2.5 times higher near the power plant than in the distant villages. When we compared the population below 18 years (young mothers) we found a factor of 3.45. When we compared with 11 year old population or lower, the factor went up to 5.7.

When we studied the survey for the last two years, we found that the stillbirths had increased, same with miscarriages or spontaneous abortions, and death of one-day old children, which cannot be attributed to infections, like diarrhoea and others, but have to do with deformities or other birth defects, or difficulties during childbirth labour.

Those accidents made the people have the dark feeling that something was wrong, because their children were born with deformities. Normally there are some 10 to 15 deformities/1000 births. This number had gone up to 40 - 50. Most people did not know what happened at their neighbours. (fig. 21 - 24)

I want to show you some slides. Here is a child with polydactyly (supplementary fingers), another with no toes at all on his feet, here is a mentally disturbed child. He was only able to walk after 4 years. Here you can see a child with microcephaly (practically no brain). Some of the fathers of those children had been working at the nuclear power plant.

The deformities are not only restricted to children, they are also seen in animals : here a goat with three legs.

I request the Jury to make a recommendation for the unborn fetuses, and for the coming generations, because what is at stake are the human rights of the mothers and the future generations. I ask you to speak on the genetic and the teratogenic effects of radiation. Thank you.

<u>The President :</u>

I thank you, Dr. Gadekar.

Now we will collect all the questions, before your responses.

I want to ask Dr. Gadekar and Ms. Hesse-Honegger a question on deformities in plants, animals and fetuses.

You have been speaking of accidental situations like Chernobyl, and of normal functioning atomic power plants. I want you to tell us if you think that normal functioning atomic plants exert negative consequences on the health and the development of fetuses, especially in the vicinity of the plants, and especially in Switzerland, where there has been no accident. As to Dr. Gadekar, I would ask her if there has been no accident in the Rajasthan atomic plant ?

Judge Mitsuo Okamoto :

In the late sixties and the early seventies, many chemical substances were used massively. Many deformities began to appear in animals, and plants. I would like to know if there is a difference between deformities due to chemicals and those due to radioactivity ? On the pictures we have seen there were Siamese twins. In Vietnam there were also Siamese twins after the use of Agent Orange. As for the Chernobyl deformities, they were due to radioactivity.

Ms. Cornelia Hesse-Honegger :

I don't think anybody in Switzerland studies the chromosome aberrations in leaf bugs living near the nuclear power plants. As for me, I am only studying the external morphology.

Dr. Sanghamitra Gadekar :

In the vicinity of the Rajasthan nuclear power plant, there is no chemical plant, where inhabitants could work, and which could provoke deformities. We see unilateral deformities. In the second generation, they are often bilateral.

I have no experience of deformities caused by chemicals. But every deformity is a consequence of a disturbed embryonic development. It varies with the damaged site, and with the stage of development, whether chemical or radiological. During the development of the embryo, there are some very critical phases for deformities.

The second question is about accidents. To my knowledge, the Indian government has never admitted to the occurrence of an accident at the Rajasthan nuclear power plant, with releases of radioactivity. The data on the releases of radioactivity in the air and in the water are not published. After a long search in libraries, we found data for certain years, for instance for 1973 to 1980, and again for 1986 to 1990. We have comparable data for a Canadian power plant with the same reactor type. This data show that releases in Rajasthan have been much higher than in Canada, up to 10 times higher or even more.

But one should not give too much credit to that data, because the numbers given for the Tritium releases are contradictory for the years 1986 and 1990.

We questioned the power plant operators. During a press conference, they first refused to reply. We pressed them and they said : "We have a shortage of personnel, so we take measures only when technicians are available". They are not releasing the actual numbers. They give only average values.

Thus we do not know if there has been an accident.

Dr. Rosalie Bertell :

I would like to come back on the previous question. Chemical substances and radiation provoke identical mutations. Muller published his first experiences in 1927. We must remember that he received the Nobel Prize in 1946 for having demonstrated radio-induced deformities. This was not some obscure research nobody had ever heard about. His results got him even the Nobel Prize !

He found that radiation produced in one month the same amount of mutations that chemicals produced during several years. They are more effective.

We are exposed to natural radioactivity, and willing or not, we are subjected to mutations similar to those produced by artificial radioactivity. When we increase the level of radioactivity in the environment, we increase the mutation rate, but they are the same mutations.

At the end of the seventies, I undertook a study in Wisconsin, where 7 nuclear power plants were functioning without incidents. I was working on sensitive indicators : the death-rate of babies born with a low weight, under 2,500 grams. Those babies present a higher mortality-rate than babies born with a higher weight. They are very sensitive indicators for the alteration of their environment. We recorded all the births of the whole state of Wisconsin, over the period, about 3 million babies.

In the downwind area, near normally functioning nuclear power plants, the death-rate of babies born with a weight under 2,500 g was increased in a statistically significant way. But that is not all. In the United States, the government publishes every year the radioactive releases of their power plants. We knew therefore the annual numbers for releases. Each time the releases increased, the death-rate also increased. When they decreased, the death-rate decreased also. As this study involved very high numbers, the findings were absolutely irrefutable. Moreover, there had be no accident during this period.

The President :

I thank you, Dr. Bertell.

Now I give the floor to Professor Erika Schuchardt, author of a book on the Children of Chernobyl.

Professor Erika Schuchardt :

I have attended the two Conferences organised in Minsk, one by the European Union, the other by the Foundation "The Children of Chernobyl". Finally, I have participated in the Conference organised in Vienna by the International Atomic Energy Agency (IAEA). I can confirm absolutely everything that has been said here.

It is absolutely intolerable to see that, 10 years after the catastrophe, the IAEA experts continue to speak about psychological problems.

There is however a little sign of hope : the Conference of the World Health Organisation (WHO) has taken place in November 1995 and the results have been reported in Vienna. If not, the IAEA would have tried to cover up everything.

Judge Freda Meissner-Blau :

Do you believe that there is a conspiracy of silence ?

Professor Erika Schuchardt :

For nearly 10 years, they spoke only of psychological problems. Today we know that this is not true. They are obliged to make some concessions.

In his speech, the representative of UNESCO spoke of the post-Chernobyl stress, and he proposed a new concept : "Environmental disorder-induced stress". But whatever they might say, everybody knows today that they are not telling everything.

With Irina Grushevaya we published a book with interviews of 1,500 children. I am pleased to present it to the Tribunal.

It is often said that the children are experiencing a cultural shock when they are invited abroad. The truth is exactly the contrary. The children who come regain some of their energy, a new beginning in their life.

Judge Freda Meissner-Blau :

I want to ask you something. Do you really believe that the IAEA has made even a small step towards reason ? I live in Vienna, we have many contacts with the IAEA and see what they are doing.

Believe me, they were obliged to organise their conference now. If they would have waited for 5 more years, they would have faced such a catastrophe, with so many diseased people, that it would have no longer been possible to organise such a conference.

I believe that the fact that the IAEA Conference was organised now, shows on the contrary that they still try to cover up the truth, for a little time, as long as it is possible for them, because we know perfectly well that the statistics on morbidity will soon rise sharply.

We must not be naive concerning the IAEA, believe me.

Professor Erika Schuchardt :

I did not say the contrary. But when you look at the documents from 1991, there are only lies. When one looks at today's documents, one can detect a very small progress, but a progress nevertheless. This is not sufficient, and this is why I am fighting and why we wrote this book on the children of Chernobyl.

The President :

Thank you. I now give the floor to Ms. Nuala Ahern, member of the European Parliament.

Ms. Nuala Ahern :

Thank you for inviting me to be present here. I am a member of the European Parliament for the Greens. I have been attending the IAEA Conference this week, and I have questioned in particular the man who has led what I will call the cover-up.

Ten years ago, over 2 million people were exposed to radioactive fallout at Chernobyl, and until now, scientists and the nuclear industry have conspired to deny that there was any damage to the health of victims of this fallout. The IAEA has been at the forefront of this cover-up.

In 1991, the IAEA published a health report, written by Dr. Frederick Mettler from New-Mexico, which said that there was no evidence of health damage, and that ill health was the result of psychological stress.

I am a psychologist, and I feel that this statement is a gross distortion of my own discipline, and I said this to Dr. Mettler, when we were discussing the issue of public trust. The IAEA authorities were saying that they have to regain public trust. I said : "You cannot gain trust if you don't deal with the reality of what happened to people. What you have done, is to try to pretend that nothing happened to these people, and they definitely do not trust you. You have distorted their reality, and if you do that, you compound the original accident by what can only be called abuse. That is what has been done."

Dr. Mettler did not reply to this. He said that he had insisted that the children should be screened and treated. That was of course a major point on the floor of the conference : because the reports of the IAEA stated that there was only psychological stress, the children were neither screened nor treated, and some of course died as a result. Dr. Mettler said that he had always insisted that the children should be screened, but that is not written in their reports.

We can thank the World Health Organisation (WHO). Some of their very eminent scientists collected clear and irrefutable documentation and evidence that there are radiation effects, and that radiation clearly affect children. We know from people who have gone there, people like Ms. Adi Roche, that the illnesses are not caused by psychological effects. We have now the work presented in November 1995 by the World Health Organisation.

What they have done to the children, they are now trying to do to the liquidators, to the 800,000 men who were drafted to do the clean-up after the accident. We have seen some of the reports at the Minsk Conference and studies from the Russian Federation. The IAEA has denied that there is a connection between radioactivity and the diseases in liquidators, and they deny that there is enough evidence.

The Ukrainian, Belarussian and Russian Federation delegations have refused to accept the figures of the IAEA, as the IAEA is denying the evidences coming from the Russian Federation on the health effects from radiation. I have told them that I will do everything that I can, to make sure that the IAEA accepts their data. Today, I have told the Chair of the IAEA Conference, Angela Merkel, Minister of the Environment of Germany, a physicist herself, that we do not accept the IAEA figures.

The IAEA is trying to say that there exists no evidence, as there are no individual data from before the accident. It is just not possible to get pre-accident data after accidents everywhere in the world.

To say that we have no evidence, is to make a mockery of the lives of many people. You cannot say this to people who have experienced these terrible diseases, who have seen their children ridden with diseases, women who now refuse to have children. One of the things that the Belorussian delegation said, that I found moving, was that women of childbearing age have moved out of the contaminated areas to the safe areas. If such a catastrophe happened in my country, it would completely devastate women. When you destroy children and mothers of childbearing age, you destroy a culture. Please let's not have this happen anywhere.

I think that the IAEA is desperate to give a life-line to the nuclear industry. Everywhere people are turning against it, even in America and the UK, where I'm mostly familiar. The global drive towards competitiveness and privatisation means that its much more difficult to covertly subsidise the nuclear industry, as has been practised in the past. Therefore they are desperate to get a life-line and their life-line today is to try to use nuclear technology to make the unsafe reactors in the East safe.

I think those should all be closed down. The European Union should spend no money on anything, except decommissioning. But the IAEA wants to keep the nuclear industry going for a few more years, and that is partly what their Conference is about. I have to say that I have reason to believe that they thought they would be successful in keeping the lid on Chernobyl and I think they now know that they have failed, because of the interest of the press and of the states, and they are dismayed at the results of their Conference.

I have a question for all the experts. Many of you have spoken of lies. I would like to know if those lies are caused by the vested interests of the nuclear-political-scientific complex, or if they are caused by the challenge this accident poses to the scientific paradigms, which is a different problem. What is your opinion on this question which, for me, is very important ?

Dr. Rosalie Bertell :

In our economy, it is very clear that scientists are dependent people. Normally scientists are paid by government or universities, and the universities are paying them with governments money, or by the industry.

The public needs information, expertise, but it is not able to afford to pay scientists to help them to understand what the argument is. In the past, society experienced this problem with respect to lawyers, and we do now have lawyers who work in the public interest. When a person has to appear before a court we provide her with a lawyer, because otherwise she can't participate. We have created a very complex technological society, but we don't provide the people, who are on the front-line of risk, with experts to help them to understand what is happening.

In 1978, I started to publish research on the health effects of low-level radiation, by ordinary diagnostic X rays. I immediately experienced a cut-off of all my funding. My name was going out on a list "Do Not Fund". In fact we even got a paper from the US National Cancer Institute, that said that, if I would like to change my line of research, they would consider refunding. I was so angry at that because it went against everything.

It was at this time that I started to look at the question of why do scientists not speak out.

There are many problems. Scientists have difficulties to publish. If you write an article on your research, that goes against the current policies, and you send it for instance to the American Public Health Association, they send it out to be reviewed by their nuclear experts, who work in the government nuclear labs. These send it back and say : "This doesn't agree with everything we know, therefore don't publish it". This makes it very difficult to publish. Your funding gets cut off, and if you are too noisy, your reputation will be attacked.

It is a very high penalty that scientists pay to speak out on these issues. They need to be protected by society. We need to recognise science working in the public interest. We need people who can speak out about a hazard, without economic and social penalties, which our society hands out very freely to them.

I think this is a fundamental question.

Ms. Solange Fernex :

I want to comment on the OECD study, which I mentioned before, which was written under the direction of Dr. H. Métivier, from the IPSN (Institute for the Protection and the Radiation Security, France). I was very saddened to read this study written by the Institute of Protection and Nuclear Safety. This is an agency that is supposed to protect us from the radiation produced by the industry, depending among others from the Ministry of Environment.

Unfortunately, in France they work very closely with the nuclear industry, because all the funding for their laboratories comes from it. Sadly, their signature covered those lies, comforting the French policy, which is an aggressive nuclear policy, selling nuclear reactors all over the world, in Asia, in Africa, in the Middle East etc....

Ms. Nuala Ahern :

Responding to your question, I think that the decisions about funding are political and not scientific decisions. We have to work very hard to make sure that European funds go into research on the effects of radiation on human beings, and not only on mice.

The second question was about the paradigm. Yes, I believe we have a problem, when it is believed that we can only have causes and effects in one-dimensional direction. Today, this is scientifically clearly out of date. A number of physicians asked why no epidemiological studies or studies on the immune system were undertaken. The IAEA responded that such studies were not relevant ! Who are they to decide?

Yet they are the decision makers.

<u>Professor Michel Fernex :</u>

I would like to make two comments concerning the ability of a chemical substance to produce deformities, which are identical to those produced by radiation. If you look at the picture of the little girl with extremely short and deformed legs, elderly persons would tell you : "This is a thalidomide child", but it is not. It is a Chernobyl child, and there are many such children. You can find collections of children with the left arm missing. Such deformities have always happened, everywhere in the world, but never such series, to be found among children of the same age, in the same community, except in places where thalidomide was prescribed to pregnant women, and today in three large countries, after Chernobyl.

During the thalidomide process, the judges could not prove that thousands of children without arms or legs, were really victims of the tablets taken by their mothers during their pregnancies. The experts said, "We do not have historical statistics, and we already have encountered children without legs before."

The IAEA expert said the same thing 2 days ago, at the Vienna Conference, using exactly the same argument : "We do not have previous statistics, so none of these deformities can be linked to the accident".

However, the difference with thalidomide, is that Belarus has excellent statistics on neonatal deformities from 1982 to this day (fig. 47). The number of deformities in this country have doubled nation-wide; some of them have even increased by a factor 10, in places where the radioactive fallout was heavy.

Unfortunately, the scientists could not speak. Professor Lasjuk is the chief of the well functioning National Genetic Institute in Minsk, with excellent computerised documentation on all deformities occurring since 14 years in Belarus. He sat in the conference room, with my report on my journey in Minsk, in which the statistics of his Institute for the years 1982 to 1994 were recorded, with all figures on deformities for which a report to the national register is compulsory, such as missing arms, spina bifida etc.. The increase incidence for these deformities is statistically significant. When the official expert from the IAEA said, "As there are no previous statistics from these

103

countries, no deformity can be related to the accident," Prof. Lazjuk was not allowed to speak.

When official IAEA experts spoke on neoplasms, claiming that only thyroid cancers in children may be related to the accident, I stood up, as a few weeks earlier, I heard Prof. Okeanov in Minsk, at the Conference organised by the Foundation for Children of Chernobyl, where he said : "The liquidators having worked more than 30 days at the exploded reactor, have a significant increase in cancers of the bladder, of the colon, and leukemia. In adult women, thyroid cancers also increased significantly". He added that there is a trend for an increase of many other cancers and illnesses.

Seeing Prof. Okeanov on the tribune in Vienna, as the judges are sitting here, in an official function, I asked "As we are discussing the relationship between radioactivity and neoplasms, I would ask Dr. Okeanov to explain his experience in this field." He did not say what he presented during his public conference in Minsk, but responded in the classical way, saying that for the time being they were studying this question but have not yet conclusive data. I was smashed[5]. But I gave the table distributed by Okeanov in Minsk to the secretariate.

It requires more than courage to speak up, especially when you are depending on money from international organisations. It may even represent, everywhere in the world, the end of a scientific or academic career.

<u>Professor Ross Hesketh :</u>

I am trained as a physicist, so when I speak now, I speak from inside of that profession.

Judge Altvater asked a question about the lies people were talking about. Has this lying to do with economic interests, or has it to do with scientific paradigms ?

Each of us goes into some chosen profession, according to his personal desires, prejudices and needs. Some people become biologists, some mathematicians, chemists, some

---

5 In the AIEA Proceedings (September 1996), this part of the discussion has totally changed. As a matter of fact, Prof. Okeanov presents now himself, at length, the data I had unsuccessfully asked him to mention.

become physicists. If you go into a university, into a position where you are in charge of a department of physicists or a department of biologists or of chemists, you realise that there are differences. People go into different professions because they are different.

Physicists are different from biologists and from mathematicians. I have worked in two universities, and the same things were very apparent in both of them. When you talk to people who have contacts with people in 4 different departments, you will find that these are different people.

10 years ago, there was a strong movement in Britain to get rid of nuclear weapons. The university near to me took out a full-page advertisement in the Times where the faculty signed a statement, saying that nuclear weapons were a very good idea, and we should keep them. That was the University of Bristol. In every university there are about 30-40 departments. In that full-page advertisement, 40% of the signatures came from the department of physics.

The President :

Thanks to you all.

I declare that this Session is adjourned for today.

Vienna, Saturday 13 April 1996

<u>The President :</u>

I declare our Session open.

5. DIRECT DAMAGE TO PEOPLE ATTRIBUTABLE TO CHERNOBYL

<u>*Speakers :*</u>
Professor Elena B. Burlakova, Semenov Institute of Chemical Physics, Russian Academy of Sciences, Moscow

Professor Yvetta N. Kogarko, Semenov Institute of Chemical Physics, Russian Academy of Sciences, Moscow

Professor Irina I. Pelevina, Semenov Institute of Chemical Physics, Russian Academy of Sciences, Moscow

Professor Ludmilla Kryzhanovskaya, Chief of the Department, Kiev Institute of Social and Forensic Psychiatry

Professor Leonid Titov, Director of the Belarusian Research Institute for Epidemiology, Immunology and Microbiology, Minsk

Professor Nika Gres, Research Institute of Radiation Medicine, Minsk

Professor Jay Gould, President of the Radiation and Public Health Project, New York (USA)

Professor Inge Schmitz-Feuerhake, Institute for Medical Physics, University of Bremen, Germany

Dr. Andreas Nidecker, Medical Radiologist, Past-President of IPPNW Switzerland, International Medical Commission on Tchernobyl, Basle

Professor Sushima Acquilla, Epidemiological Department, University of Newcastle-on-Tyne, United Kingdom

I give the floor to Professor Burlakova.

Professor Elena B. Burlakova :

First of all, I would like to thank you for your invitation, and for the possibility to present our data. The data from this Tribunal's sessions will be more important than those of the IAEA Conference. Nevertheless, I am surprised that all the data we obtained in our investigations of different biophysical and biochemical factors, in liquidators and in children, do not interest the IAEA. For them, the determination of the radiogenic nature of any disease must show a linear dose-dependent effect. Only when this linear dose-dependence exists, can one talk about the radiogenic nature of an effect.

Long before the Chernobyl accident, we studied the effects of low doses of radiation, and did not find any linear dependence. It is incorrect to conclude that there are no effects from low-level radiation. Since the beginning of our investigations on the effects of low doses of radiation, we found a non linear dose-dependence, which is not a monotone, but in many cases, a bimodal dependence. That means that when we increase the radiation dose, the effect decreases, before increasing again. With higher doses, the effect may be less than what we obtained with lower doses. The effect can change sign.

Our data shows that the absence of an linear dependence, does not mean the absence of dose-dependence nor that this effect is not radiogenic. Some people have another opinion - they think that the absence of linear and monotone dependence on the dose, proves non-radiogenic effects. So all diseases depend only on psychological stress and not on radiation. This is the main position of the IAEA.

The IAEA may admit that the number of diseases increases, but not due to radiation, only to psychological stress. This allows us to build atomic stations, and to deal with waste. Everybody can receive low doses, without consequences and all is well. The psychological stress is caused by TV programs, newspapers, discussions and conferences.

Our experiments with animals, and then our parallel investigations with people, show the radiogenic nature of biochemical and biophysical changes, which cause all the diseases observed in our countries.

These figures (fig. 28, 29) reflects the changes in the electrophoresis of lipids in cell membranes, and in the structure of the genome, caused by an increase of ionising radiation, beginning with extremely small doses. We can see that we have no linear dose-dependence, this is from experiments on animals.

The same effect is found with 6 centiGy and 180 centiGy. With intermediate doses, the effects are much lower. This data shows that the efficiency of low doses is higher than that of higher doses.

We can explain this phenomenon with the processes of repair. After an exposure to very low doses of radiation, the process of repair is not induced. We can observe a very great number of disturbances, without any process of reparation.

We presented this data to our scientific community, and our contradictors told us : "You only based your data on animals, and people are not animals". Saying this, they knew perfectly well that it was not possible, for obvious ethical reasons, to make experiments with increasing doses of radiation on humans.

After Chernobyl, we investigated the biophysical and biochemical variations in liquidators. We again found that in many cases, there is no linear dose-dependent effect, especially with regard to the changes in chromosomal aberrations.

We investigated the variations in different biochemical characteristics, for example, Vitamin A and E, lipids peroxidation, the incidence of free radicals and so on. We then compared our data on the changes in the anti-oxydant status of the organism, which is responsible for the resistance to radiation, to the changes in the immunological status.

The variations of the immunological characteristics and of the anti-oxydant status show the same dose-dependence. Same for the incidence of chromosomal disturbances and anti-oxydant status changes. In both cases, very low doses induce maximal changes as compared to the control group. The same situation exists again as regard to the immunological status, 10-15 centiGy induce the first peak of changes.

The health of our liquidators and children has undergone

very great changes, with an increase of morbidity for different diseases. It is very interesting to note that for the children and for the liquidators, the changes in the state of health follow the same pattern. This is in absolute contradiction with a psychological nature of these diseases.

We investigated the dose-dependence in various diseases of the liquidators. The changes in the number of vascular, cardiovascular diseases, digestive diseases, neural diseases follow the same pattern : their dependence on the dose has the same character, with a maximum between 6 to 10 centiGy.

The same situation was found in a study of diseases leading to total invalidity : the maximum effect is found between 10 and 15 centiGy. The cancer mortality among liquidators shows the same dose dependence. With leukemia, we note a peak for doses of 0 to 5 centiGy, very low doses. The same situation exists for digestive disorders, for the cancer of the stomach.

So my conclusion is that the dose-dependent effect is not linear for very low doses. It is a more complicated dependence. But the official policy today is such, that if a physician cannot show a monotonic increase of a disease, with increasing doses, this proves the non radiogenic nature of this disease. It is therefore forbidden to think and to speak of a radiogenic nature of these diseases.

The reality is however, and this is my second conclusion, that very low doses of radiation can induce the same diseases as much higher doses.

My third conclusion is the following : the fact that we can observe similar changes in the health of children, of liquidators and of victims of the atomic bomb, proves the radiogenic nature of these diseases in contaminated areas (fig. 30, 31). Consequently, they are not caused by psychological stress.

Psychological stress does exist, as the situation is very critical, but it is not the main cause of these diseases. Thank you very much.

The President :

Thank you, Professor Burlakova.

I now give the floor to Professor Kogarko.

Professor Yvetta N. Kogarko :

We are very happy to be here today to present to the Tribunal problems, that the IAEA says do not exist at all.

The effects on the environment of the Chernobyl atomic catastrophe, have been investigated many times, and from different points of view, during the 10 years since the accident. Investigations have been performed on the pollution of the air, the soil, the river and ground waters. But investigations of the effects of different radiation doses, at different times, on the human organisms, have had no priority.

The radiation pollution zone includes 138 administrative regions, inhabited by over 3 million people. Citizens of the Bryanskaya, Tulskaya, Kalujskaya regions of the Russian Federation were affected most seriously.

The increase of acute and chronic leukemias in regions affected by the radiological contamination after the catastrophe, and the poor efficiency of prophylactic measures and early diagnostics, shows how important it is to work on the detection of early signs of leukemia transformation in "hemogenic" cells, at the molecular-genetic level, in patients living in radiation pollution regions. The solution of this problem needs the combined efforts of medicine, biology and ecology.

I will present to the Tribunal data :

- on cases of lymphoproliferative diseases (LPD) - 50 patients,
- chronic lympholeucosis (CHLL) - 30 patients,
- malignant lymphoma (ML) - 20 patients, who lived in unfortunate regions of Russia (Bryanskaya, Kalujskaya, Tulskaya regions).

Comparative dynamic researches were also performed in 3 groups of 50 people, from which we have excluded patients already suffering from leukemia in 1987.

These three groups are following :

- patients showing initial disease signs,
- patients presenting a clinical picture of leukemia,
- patients treated by specific chemotherapeutic agents

Our investigations covered the period from 1987 to 1993.

In the case of LPD, the development of blood lymphocytes is

110

on the whole stopped at some stage, but they are also capable of proliferating. Changes occur in the chemical composition, the structure and the properties of various cell components : membranes, cytoplasmic structures and the nucleus.

A whole range of modern methods must be used for the determination of the malignant transformation of the lymphocytes, for instance : radio-autography, using labelled nucleic acid precursors, scanning, micro-spectrophotometry, nuclear magnetic resonance.

We studied the changes in the membranes of lymphocytes in patients with lymphoproliferative diseases and lymphomas.

We performed investigations on the dynamic of lipids membranes of lymphocytes, in patients suffering from chronic LL and ML. As controls, we used lymphocytes of normal people, of patients suffering from myocarditis, from non cancerous diseases associated with leuko- and lymphocytosis, and from a tumour genesis disease with red cell damage.

The characters of the dynamic change of the membrane lipids in lymphocytes, was determined by the H1 NMR spectroscopy method of high resolution, at 250 MHz and 360 MHz frequencies. The following parameters were used to characterise the molecular changes in the lipids : A1= 0.89 and A2 = 3.21 (A1 are protons of methyl groups in the fatty acid chains, and A2 are protons of methyl groups of phosphatydilcholine polar heads, respectively), which may reflect differences in the composition of the lipids in the cell membrane. Each of the above mentioned pathologies possess specific features in the spectra of the membranes of their blood lymphocytes.

If compared with the controls, ChLL and ML present an increase of the intensity of the amplitude of the A1 and A2 signals, and narrowing Ch group proton signals, which show the presence of lipids with a higher molecular mobility. Such changes of the stereogram are characteristic for the lymphocyte cytoplasmic membrane lipids, at early stages of ChLL and ML, and they remain constant during the progression of the diseases. The graphics of the results obtained, form two strictly limited, non crossing ranges, which include the data for the norm and ChLL each (fig. 45).

This method can be successfully applied for an early and differentiated ChLL diagnosis. The results for ML and other pathologies are very different and they possess no strictly specific characters.

It is clear that all the disturbances of the immunogenesis processes and of the hemogenesis system are accelerated in extreme conditions. Radioactive pollution of soil, water, food, were present where patients affected by the initial stage of disease and LPD were living. This causes the increase of the number of LPD patients (10% to 18%), a more serious evolution of the disease (up to 65%), the decrease of remission-time (up to 73%), and the decrease of the patients life-time.

This new bio-molecular approach to the study of the consequences of the Chernobyl catastrophe, by the method of H1 NMR spectroscopy of blood lymphocytes, allows us to perform individual and mass screenings of populations living in contaminated zones.

This permits us to detect alterations in circulating blood lymphocyte at early LPD stages, before any clinical symptoms of the disease can be detected. This method of human blood analysis provides very fast (6 hours), and statistically proven results, and makes possible the rapid screening of many people, affected by different physical and chemical agents present in their environment, and the detection of "risk groups" in populations living in radiation pollution zones. This new method of evaluation of the human hematopoietic system, that can be generalised, allows early LPD diagnosis.

It is now necessary to propose a new approach to the situation created by the Chernobyl catastrophe. We should not only register facts and be content. It is very important to propose a special diagnostic procedure for leukemia, to form groups of high risk for this sickness, and to perform special investigations for the monitoring of those people.

I want to propose to laboratories in the United States, Japan, Canada, India and others, co-operative studies on the monitoring by nuclear magnetic resonance of the blood cells in leukemia cases.

This will make it easier to state not only the number of leukemias and leukoses, but also to demonstrate in a very objective way, the influence of the radiation on the leucoses affecting the people, their incidence and their evolution.

The President :

Thank you very much, Professor Kogarko.

I now give the floor to Professor Pelevina.

Professor Irina I. Pelevina :

After the Chernobyl catastrophe, a specific ecological situation has developed, which is very similar to a post-atomic war situation. A very large area is contaminated by radio-isotopes with a very long period, and many people inhabit this region. Many places are contaminated by the so-called "hot particles" and other radionuclides, and the people are suffering from the combined effects of this contamination.

In this ecological catastrophe of Chernobyl, what is to be considered as a low dose ? What is a low dose ?

Five years after the Chernobyl catastrophe, I undertook investigations, using cell cultures from mice, and lymphocytes from patients living in the Bryansk region, one of the most contaminated areas in Russia, up to 40 Curie/km2. I wanted to study the adaptive mechanisms in the lymphocytes, by a method which is also used by Japanese scientists in areas contaminated by Chernobyl in Belarus.

Cell cultures, (He La cells), exposed to doses of about O,1 centiGy in the Chernobyl zone, present an increase in their proliferative activities. We have found genetic anomalies in cells exposed to Chernobyl radiation.

The increase of the radiosensitivity, noted in cells exposed in the contaminated zone is a new finding.

We studied the survival of :
- cells exposed to an acute irradiation in the laboratory
- cells exposed in the contaminated zone
- the same cells, exposed to a secondary acute irradiation in the laboratory.

The increase of the radiosensitivity of exposed cells is shown by their rate of survival and by their chromosomic aberrations. The lesions in the germinal cells depend on the dose and the duration of the exposition.

When we placed mice in the contaminated zone, and irradiated them afterwards in the laboratory, we noticed an increase of the radiosensitivity of their bone-marrow cells. We exposed pregnant mice in the zone, and realised cell cultures with cells taken from their embryos. We found chromosomic aberrations, genetic anomalies.

Following conclusion can be drawn from these results :

In the contaminated zone, low doses of radiation induce a genetic instability, anomalies of the genome, transmissible during many generations from the irradiated cells. This instability of the genome can express itself in lethal effects.

We noticed that the cells which pose problems, are not those which have been acutely irradiated, but those which were submitted to a prolonged exposition to low doses of radiation.

Study on lymphocytes :

We studied also lymphocytes from persons living in the contaminated zone, and we could show that low doses of radiation induce a kind of "allergic" effect, of hypersensitivity. This is a protective defence mechanism against environmental pollutants.

We can find adaptive forms in the lymphocytes of people who live in the contaminated zone. These figures (fig. 32, 33) show micronuclei, which are genetic alterations in the lymphocytes of practically all patients living in the Bryansk region. Here in persons exposed to low doses, here in persons exposed to higher doses.

In the contaminated zone, the adaptive response is decreasing. On this figure we see cells of persons presenting a very high sensitivity to high radiation doses. Children living in highly contaminated areas of the Bryansk zone, present a sensitivity which is even higher than that of adults.

In the same region, we can see in children an increase of cells with chromosomic aberrations (fig 34, 35), signs of an increase of the radiosensitivity. The increase of those aberrations in children, as compared to adults, is parallel to the increase of their radiosensitivity, and to the absence of any adaptive response.

We note an absence of adaptive responses in many patients living in the contaminated zones. The adaptive response can be more or less strongly impaired. There are persons where the adaptive response is totally suppressed, with an increase of their radiosensitivity.

Of dozens of children living in a very contaminated village, only 5 show an adaptive response. The others present an increase of their radiosensitivity. Life in the contaminated zone leads consequently to a weakening of the natural defence mechanisms (fig. 36, 37), by which the organism is able to defend itself from many diseases, tumours and infectious diseases.

Conclusion : the specific new ecological situation leads to a new population of animals and humans, having an increased sensitivity to several factors : radioactivity, pollution, chemicals, infectious diseases, medical treatments etc.

The President :

Thank you very much, Professor Pelevina.

I give the floor to Dr. Bertell.

Dr. Rosalie Bertell :

The summaries of the testimonies have been distributed. There you will find the figures and the bibliography.

Professor Burlakova has presented to the Tribunal a copy of the book of which she is Editor : "Consequences of the Chernobyl Catastrophe : Human Health". In this book, Professor Burlakova and 14 other scientists publish their findings in animal and human studies on the health effects of low-dose, slow-dose rate exposure to ionising radiation. They examined carefully the following biological phenomena, under ionising-radiation exposure situations :

- alkaline elution of DNA of lymphocytes and liver cells,
- neutral elution and adsorption of spleen DNA on nitrocellulose filters,
- restriction of spleen DNA by EcoRi endonuclease,
- structural characteristics (using the ESR spin probe technique) of nuclear, mitochondrial, synaptic, erythrocyte and leukocyte membranes
- activity and isoforms of aldolase and lactate hydrogenase enzymes,
- activity of acetylcholine esterase, superoxide dismutase and glutathione peroxidase

Legends of the figures :

1. Leaf bug collected in Gavle, Sweden, (Chernobyl fallout) : segments from left antenna are missing. (drawing : C. Hesse-Honegger)

2. Drosophile collected in Southern Switzerland, (Chernobyl fallout): the first generation shows a deformed clumped wing. (drawing : C. Hesse-Honegger)

3. Bug from Gösgen (downwind Swiss commercial atomic reactor) : shortened right wing. (drawing : C. Hesse-Honegger)

4. Two leaf bug larva from Switzerland (near Paul Scherrer research reactor) : the right wing of the left leaf bug is too short. At the right, damaged wing and displaced scutellum. (drawing : C. Hesse-Honegger)

5. Bug from Switzerland (near Paul Scherrer research reactor) : At the right, deformed scutum. (drawing : C. Hesse-Honegger)

6. Bug from the South of the 30 km zone in Chernobyl : deformed left side of the scutum, irregular black design. (drawing : C. Hesse-Honegger)

7. Bug from Polesskoie (Chernobyl fallout) : missing segments on left antenna. (drawing : C. Hesse-Honegger)

8. Two bugs from Sellafield : deformations and irregular black dots. (drawing : C. Hesse-Honegger)

9. Of the 9 carp, only one is normal (white). The recessive violet mutation, breeded i some fish-farms in Germany, was formerly very rare in Belarus. Note the various deformities of caudal, anal and dorsal fin, and of the mouth (4th from below). (photo : A. Slukvin)

10. Deformities in 6 months old carp (dorsal and caudal fin, scales, etc.). (photo : A. Slukvin)

11. Violet mutation in carp. The upper carp has no dorsal fin, the lower no opercule. (photo : A. Slukvin)

12. Of the three carp shown in a ventral position, the two upper ones show no pigment, which reveals their skeleton. (photo : A. Slukvin)

13. A tender moment for Natasha and her mother. Natasha is alive because of a life-saving operation in Germany. (photo : Anatoly Kleshuk)

14. Intubation after operation of facial deformities. This child with severe multiple deformities died soon after this operation (Belarus). (photo : Anatoly Kleshuk)

15. Tumours are increasing, even in early childhood. This child from Belarus was successfully operated in Ireland. (photo : Adi Roche)

16. Brain deformities and anencephalia have doubled in Belarus after Chernobyl. (photo : Adi Roche)

17. Five year old retarded and deformed children have to leave the pediatric clinic for the children's psychiatric wards, where their days are counted (Belarus). (photo : Adi Roche)

18. Malignancies can be operated. amputations followed by chemotherapy. A heavy burden for a poor country such as Belarus. (photo : Adi Roche)

19. 70 % of children cancers have acceptable prognoses. Surgeons perform an excellent work in Belarus. However children after operation for thyroid cancer face difficult, life-long hormonal treatments (Belarus). (photo : Adi Roche)

20. Serenity and spirituality embodied in little Nastya, awaiting anxiously to be taken for long-term care to Ireland. (photo : Anatoly Kleshuk)

21. Prevalence of congenital malformations in children from different age groups, living in proximate or distant villages from a nuclear power plant in Rajasthan. (Dr. Gadekar)

22. Pregnancy outcome in proximate or distant villages from a nuclear power plant in Rajasthan. (Dr. Gadekar)

23. Deaths and deformities among infants during 1993 and 1994, in proximate or distant villages from a nuclear power plant in Rajasthan. (Dr. Gadekar)

24. Type of deformities by system among children born in proximate of distant villages from a nuclear power plant. (Dr. Gadekar)

25. Distribution in percent of internal and external exposure in Chernobyl children, expressed in total effective dose equivalent. (Dr. Gres)

26. Comparison of degree of stomach mucosa atrophy in 4 groups of children exposed to different environmental pollution : nitrates, radiation, lead, and the combination of the three after Chernobyl, indicating potentiation. (Dr. Gres)

27. Atrophy, intestinal metaplasia and atrophy + intestinal metaplasia in Chernobyl children, compared with controls. (Dr. Gres)

28. Bi-modal curves (-----: spleen DNA, _____ : microviscosity of exposed mouse liver) depending on the dos of radiation (intensity : 41 x 10 -3 mGy.min -1). Similar peaks at 60, respectively 120, and 1800 mGy. (Prof. Burlakova)

29. Bi-modal curves of binding of the exposed mice spleen DNA depending on the dose of irradiation (-----: low-dose rate : 4.1 x 10 -3 mGy.min -1, _____ : high-dose rate : 41 x 10 -3 mGy.min -1). (Prof. Burlakova)

30. Leukemia death rate for people after atomic bombing and nuclear accidents, and among workers in the nuclear industry (the numbers in the table correspond to the numbers of the points in fig. 31). (Prof. Burlakova)

31. Leukemia deaths per 100,000 persons/year, depending on the dose of radiation (the numbers of the points correspond to the numbers in fig 30). (Prof. Burlakova)

32. Lymphocyte with a tailed nucleus (sign of irradiation) in a blood smear. (Prof. Pelevina)

33. Schema of the formation of cells with tailed nuclei during cell division. (Prof. Pelevina)

34. Dose-response curve for frequency of lymphocytes with tailed nuclei (FLTN) in the peripheral blood of B ALB/C mice, with increasing radiation doses, in Gy. (Prof. Pelevina)

35. Frequency of the peripheral blood lymphocytes with tailed nuclei (FLTN) in the radiation-exposed persons compared with non-irradiated persons. (Prof. Pelevina)

36. Three T-lymphocytes subpopulations content in spleen of mice 15 days after exposure in the zone of the Chernobyl accident. I : Lyt 1+,L3T4, II : Lyt 2+, III L 1, 2+. (Prof. Pelevina)

37. Lyt I+/Lyt 2+ cell ratio in peripheral blood (I), and spleen (2), of mice, 15 days after stay in the zone of the

Chernobyl accident, with increased absorbed radiation dose (in Gy). Such alteration may change the immune response. (Prof. Pelevina)

38. The dynamics of T-lymphocytes (%) content in different age groups of children from Bragin district. The initial drop was only partially compensated. (Prof. Titov)

39. Significant drop in the concentration of immunoglobulin A isotype in two groups of children out of four after Chernobyl. (Prof. Titov)

40. Concentration of the main classes of immunoglobulins in saliva of children living in the territories with different levels of contamination with CS 137. (Prof. Titov)

41. Becquerels per litre of Iodine 131 and Cesium 137 in pasteurized milk, Hanford, Connecticut, USA, 1983-90. (Prof. Gould)

42. Age-adjusted thyroid cancer incidence rate per 100.000/year, adjusted to 1970 US Standard; Connecticut, Iowa and Utah, 1985-89 to 1990-93. (Prof. Gould)

43. Thyroid cancer cases, all ages and sexes; Middlesex and New London counties, Connecticut, USA, (1950-93, rise since the begining of the nuclear age). (Prof. Gould)

44. Diseases for which A-Bomb victims were treated, compared with the general public in Japan. (Dr. Furitsu)

45. Early bio-molecular detection, by nuclear-magnetic-resonnance test, of changes in the lipid membran of blood lymphocytes, before the appearance of any clinical sign of lymphoid leukemia. Controls are clearly separated from the lymphoid leukemias. (Prof. Kogarko)

46. Incidence of obligatory registered malformation in Belarus from 1982 to 1993 (per 1000 neonates) (* indicates statistically significantly increased after the Chernobyl catastrophe). (Prof. Lazjuk)

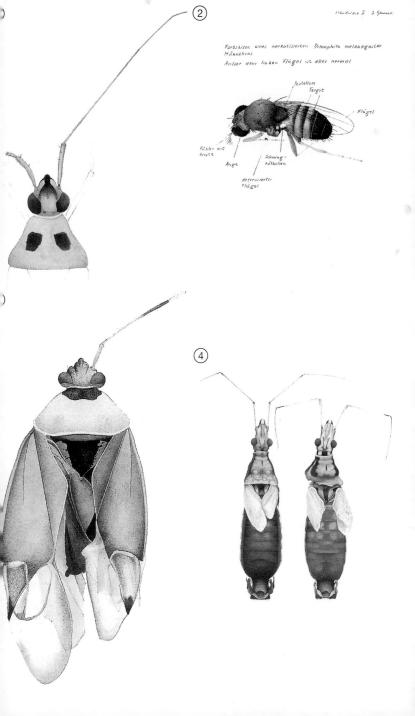

Farbskizze eines narkotisierten *Drosophila melanogaster* Männchens

Ausser dem linken Flügel ist alles normal

Scutellum
Tergit
Flügel
Fühler mit Arista
Auge
Schwing-hölbchen
deformierter Flügel

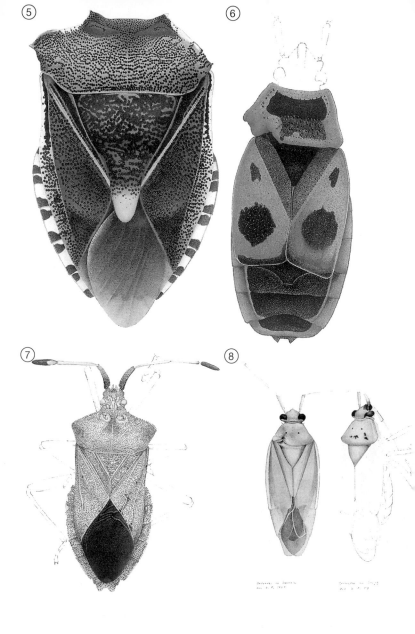

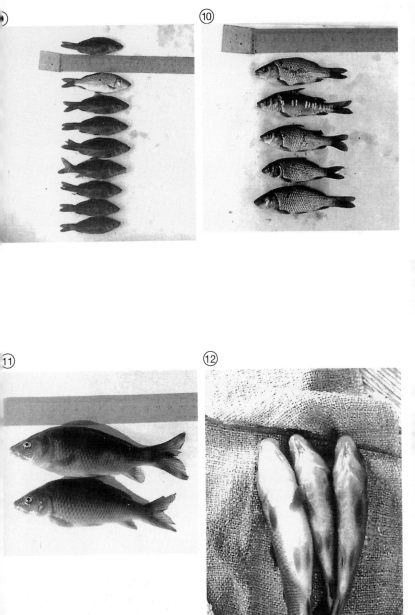

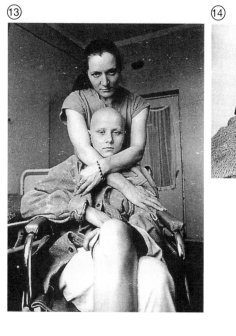

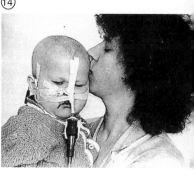

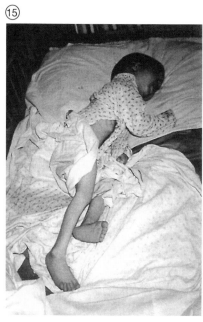

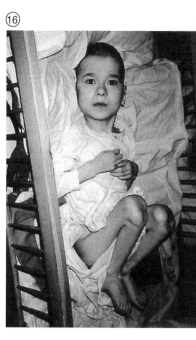

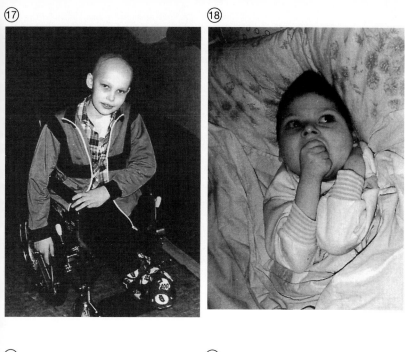

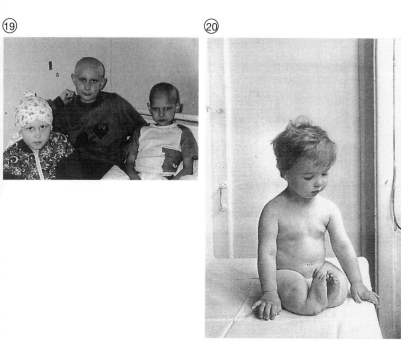

PREVALENCE OF CONGENITAL MALFORMATIONS

		Deformities in Children less than 11 years of age		Deformities in population less than 18 years of age		Deformities in population more than 18 years of age		Deformities in the total population	
		Males	Females	Males	Females	Males	Females	Males	Females
Proximate Villages	Population	462	450	736	697	754	673	1490	1370
	Deformities	24	9	29	10	3	2	32	12
Distant Villages	Population	421	421	625	642	659	618	1284	1260
	Deformities	5	1	8	2	3	1	11	3

There are five cases of multiple deformities in proximate villages, four with two each and one with three.

PREGNANCY OUTCOME IN THE LAST TWO YEARS

	Live Born		Stillborn		Total Births*	Abortions**	Currently Pregnant
	With Deformity	Without Deformity	With Deformity	Without Deformity			
Proximate Villages	16	236	4	2	258	27	31
Distant Villages	3	194	0	0	197	5	29

*Includes 3 pairs of twins in both areas
**Between 8 weeks to 28 weeks of pregnancy

DEATHS AMONGST INFANTS DURING THE LAST TWO YEARS

		Stillbirths	One Day Deaths	Early Neonatal Deaths	Infant Mortality
Proximate Villages	Expected*	1.9	—	8.2	28.2
	Observed	6	7	13	32
Distant Villages	Expected*	1.5	—	6.5	22.6
	Observed	0	1	5	19

*Expected on the basis of census data for the area (See References 14 and 15)

TYPES OF DEFORMITIES

Types of Deformities	PROXIMATE VILLAGES		DISTANT VILLAGES	
	Male	Female	Male	Female
CENTRAL NERVOUS SYSTEM	3	1	0	0
MENTAL RETARDATION, DEAFNESS	4	3	2	2
SENSE ORGANS *	10	5	3	1
GENITO-URINARY SYSTEM **	4	1	0	0
MUSKULO-SKELETAL SYSTEM	15	1	5	0

*two cases with ear lobe groves and two cases with auditory miatus absent and varied deformity of pinna

** one case of polycystic kidney diagnosed at civil hospita, Kota

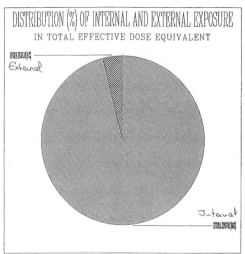

25

DISTRIBUTION (%) OF INTERNAL AND EXTERNAL EXPOSURE
IN TOTAL EFFECTIVE DOSE EQUIVALENT

External

Internal

26

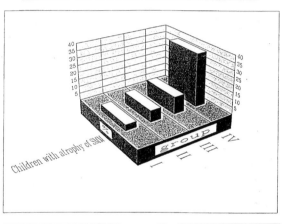

Children with atrophy of SMM

group

I   II   III   IV

27

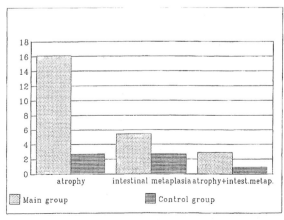

atrophy   intestinal metaplasia atrophy+intest.metap.

Main group   Control group

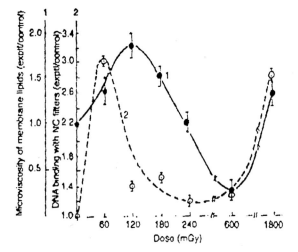

Curve 1, per cent binding of the spleen DNA with
nitrocellulose filters (relative units); and curve 2, microviscosity of nuclear membrane lipids of the exposed mouse
liver depending on the dose of radiation (intensity of radiation,
41×10^{-3} mGy.min^{-1}).

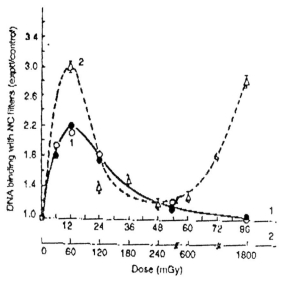

Per cent of binding of the exposed mice spleen DNA
with nitrocellulose filters depending on the dose of irradiation
(in relative units). Curves: (1) dose rate 4.1×10^{-3} mGy.min^{-1};
(2) dose rate 41×10^{-3} mGy.min^{-1}.

The data on the leukaemia death rate for people after atomic bombing and nuclear accidents and for worker in the nuclear industry (the numbers in the table correspond to the numbers of the points in Figure 5).

Irradiation locality	Dose (mSv)	Leucoses death rate per 10^5 person.years	Ref.
1. Pilgrim 1983–1988	2	3.6*	19
2. UKAEA workers 1946–1979	20 (20–50)	4.3*	15
3. Pilgrim 1979–1983	20	14.4*	19
4. Oakridge National Laboratory	21	10.4	16
5. Hanford	27	6	16
6. American Military Agency	27.6	2.5	16
7. Residents of Japan Group I	30	5.1	17
8. American Nuclear Agency	33.1	5.6	16
9. Rockyflats	35	4.0	16
10. UKAEA workers	50	5.22	15
11. Residents of Japan Group II	80	1.4	17
12. UKAEA workers	100	3.0*	15
13. Sellafield	139	4.2	16
14. Residents of Japan Group III	150	5.7	17
15. Residents at the Techa River, Group I	176	3.8	18
16. Residents at the Techa River, Group II	180	6.9	18
17. Residents at the Techa River, Group III	290	8.5	18
18. Residents of Japan Group IV	400	8.56	17
19. Residents at the Techa River, Group IV	610	6.5 (14.3*)	18
20. Residents at the Techa River, Group V	780	7.9 (17.3*)	18
21. Residents of Japan Group V	800	14.3	17
22. Residents at the Techa River, Group VI	1640	15.3	18
23. Residents of Japan Group VI	1800	28.6	17
24. Residents of Japan Group VII	2600	57	17
25. Residents of Japan Group VIII	3600	91	17

*The data are related to the control of 3.6 per 10^5 person.years

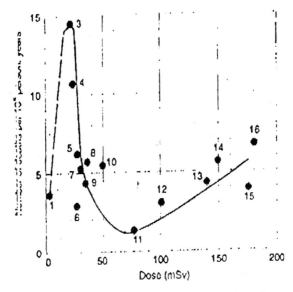

Leukaemia deaths per 10^5 person.years depending on the dose of radiation (the numbers of the points correspond to the numbers in Table 4).

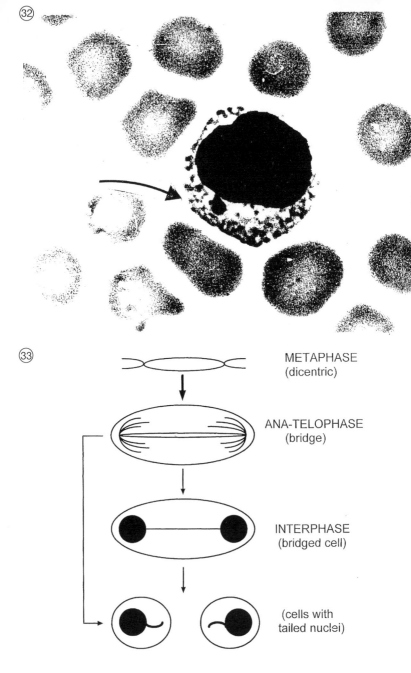

METAPHASE
(dicentric)

ANA-TELOPHASE
(bridge)

INTERPHASE
(bridged cell)

(cells with
tailed nuclei)

Scheme of formation of cells with tailed nuclei

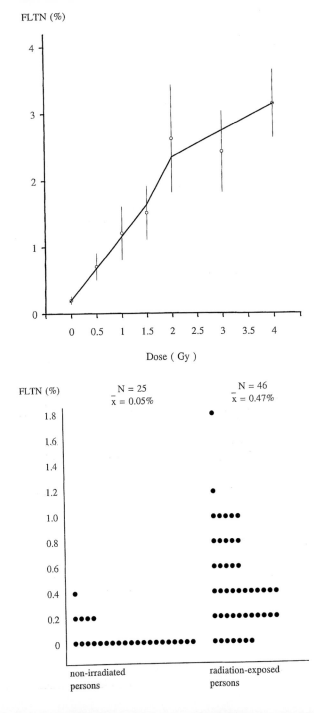

FLTN (%)

Dose (Gy)

FLTN (%)

$\overline{N} = 25$
$\overline{x} = 0.05\%$

$\overline{N} = 46$
$\overline{x} = 0.47\%$

non-irradiated
persons

radiation-exposed
persons

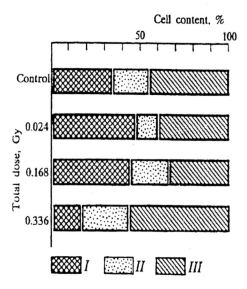

36

T-lymphocyte subpopulation content in spleen of mice 15 days after exposure in the zone of the Chernobyl accident. *I* – Lyt1⁺, L3T4, *II* – Lyt2⁺, *III* – L1⁺, 2⁺.

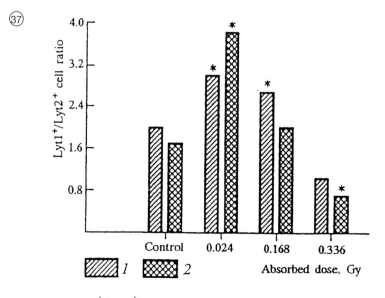

37

Lyt1⁺/Lyt2⁺ cell ratio in peripheral blood (*1*) and spleen (*2*) of mice 15 days after stay in the zone of the Chernobyl accident.

38. The dynamics of T-lymphocytes (%) content in different age groups of children from Bragin district

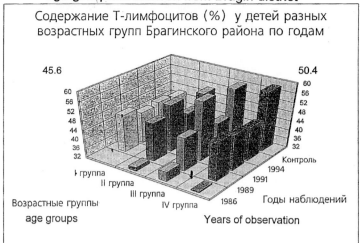

Содержание Т-лимфоцитов (%) у детей разных возрастных групп Брагинского района по годам

45.6   50.4

Возрастные группы
age groups

I группа
II группа
III группа
IV группа

Контроль
1994
1991
1989
1986

Годы наблюдений
Years of observation

39.

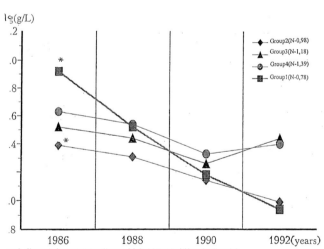

Ig(g/L)

- Group2(N-0,98)
- Group3(N-1,18)
- Group4(N-1,39)
- Group1(N-0,78)

1986   1988   1990   1992(years)

ure 3. Changes in the concentration of immunoglobulin A isotype in children after Chernobyl.

40.

Concentration of the Main Classes of Immunoglobulins in Saliva of Children Living in the Territories with Different Levels of Contamination with Cs 137

Groups of Children	Immunoglobulins (g/l)			
	IgG	IgA	IgAs	IgM
1st	0.16±0.02	0.13±0.01	0.61±0.05	0.07±0.009
2nd	0.18±0.04	0.20±0.05	0.68±0.22	0.08±0.01
3rd	0.36±0.05	0.22±0.05	0.64±0.07	0.11±0.01
4th	0.39±0.04	0.32±0.02	0.84±0.04	0.08±0.009
5th	0.21±0.06	0.13±0.02	0.97±0.08	0.08±0.007
P (1–4)	<0.01	<0.01	<0.05	>0.05
P (1–5)	>0.05	>0.05	<0.001	>0.05

Becquerels per litre of iodine-131 and caesium-137 in pasteurized milk; Hartford, Connecticut, USA, 1983–90

Year	No. of readings	Average radioactivity (Bq/l)	
		I^{131}	Cs^{137}
1983	12	0.01	0.05
1984	12	0.00	0.08
1985	11	0.03	0.10
1986			
Jan–Apr	4	0.08	0.07
5 May–22 May	6	0.30	0.13
27 May–23 Jun	5	0.63	0.49
Jul–Dec	6	0.08	0.25
1987	12	0.10	0.23
1988	11	0.10	0.18
1989	11	0.09	0.08
1990	8	0.18	0.17

Age-adjusted thyroid cancer incidence rate per 100,000 adjusted to 1970 US Standard; Connecticut, Iowa and Utah, 1985–89 to 1990–93

State	No. of cases		Rate		
	1985–89	1990–93[a]	1985–89	1990–93[a]	% change
Utah	412	393	5.36	6.07	13.1*
Iowa	684	640	4.32	5.14	18.8**
Connecticut	642	666	3.45	4.35	26.2†
Total	1738	1699	4.13	4.93	19.4†

*$P < 0.10$.
**$P < 0.01$.
†$P < 0.0001$.
[a] 4 years.

Thyroid cancer cases, all ages and sexes; Middlesex and New London counties, Connecticut, USA, 1950–93

Year	No. of cases in county	Crude rate			
		County		Rest of state	
Middlesex county					
1950–52[a]	4	1.92	(–)	2.15	(–)
1953–57	9	2.30	(+19.8%)	1.92	(−10.7%)
1958–62	10	2.25	(−2.2%)	2.40	(+25.0%)
1963–67	13	2.55	(+13.3%)	2.46	(+2.5%)
(Haddam Neck reactor start-up)					
1968–72	14	2.44	(−4.3%)	2.86	(+16.3%)
1973–77	23	3.77	(+54.7%)	3.38	(+18.2%)
1978–82	23	3.57	(−5.3%)	3.47	(+2.7%)
1983–87	30	4.41	(+23.5%)	4.20	(+21.0%)
1988–92	26	3.63	(−17.7%)	4.61	(+9.8%)
New London county					
1951–55	15	1.91	(–)	2.06	(–)
1956–60	14	1.57	(−17.8%)	1.97	(−4.4%)
1961–65	17	1.71	(+8.9%)	2.39	(+21.3%)
1966–70	17	1.54	(−9.9%)	2.75	(+15.0%)
(Millstone reactor start-up)					
1971–75	20	1.72	(+11.7%)	3.04	(+10.5%)
1976–80	38	3.21	(+86.8%)*	3.41	(+12.2%)
1981–85	42	3.45	(+7.4%)	4.04	(+18.5%)
1986–90	62	4.93	(+42.9%)	4.24	(+5.0%)
1991–93[a]	51	6.69	(+35.7%)	4.98	(+17.5%)

*$P < 0.05$.
[a] 3 years.

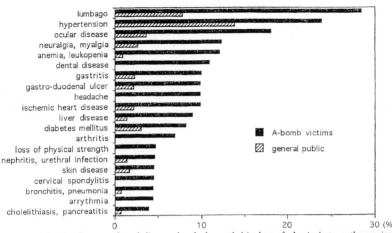

Diseases for which A-bomb victims have taken medical care
--compared with the general public

- lumbago
- hypertension
- ocular disease
- neuralgia, myalgia
- anemia, leukopenia
- dental disease
- gastritis
- gastro-duodenal ulcer
- headache
- ischemic heart disease
- liver disease
- diabetes mellitus
- arthritis
- loss of physical strength
- nephritis, urethral infection
- skin disease
- cervical spondylitis
- bronchitis, pneumonia
- arrythmia
- cholelithiasis, pancreatitis

■ A-bomb victims
▨ general public

*As for the diseases; dental disease, headache, arthritis, loss of physical strength, cervical spondylitis and arrythmia, we cannot get the corresponding standards in "the basic national life survey."

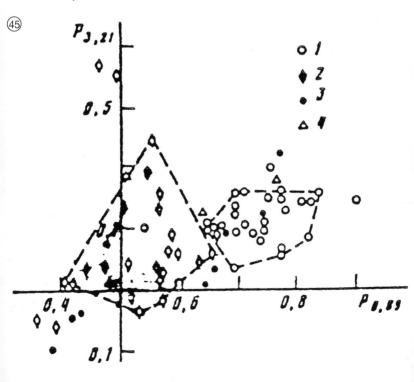

Incidence of Obligatory Registered Malformations in Belarus for 1982 to 1993 (per 1000 neonates)

Malformation	Areas contaminated with Cs-137				Control (30 regions)	
	>15 Ci/km^2 17 regions		>1 Ci/km^2 54 regions			
	1982-1985	1987-1993	1982-1985	1987-1993	1982-1985	1987-1993
Anencephaly	0.28	0.35	0.24	0.54*	0.35	0.37
Spina bifida	0.58	0.76	0.67	0.83*	0.64	0.84
Cleft lip and/or palate	0.63	0.99	0.70	0.90	0.50	0.91*
Polydactyly	0.10	1.01*	0.30	0.60*	0.26	0.47*
Limb reduction defects	0.15	0.43*	0.18	0.32*	0.20	0.19
Oesophageal atresia	0.08	0.10	0.12	0.16	0.11	0.12
Anorectal atresia	0.05	0.08	0.08	0.09	0.03	0.07
Down's syndrome	0.91	0.82	0.86	1.02	0.63	0.98*
Multiple malformations	1.04	2.40*	1.41	2.10*	1.18	1.47
Total	3.87	6.94*	4.57	6.56*	3.90	5.43*
	151	338	899	1882	255	565
Per cent increase before and after	79		44		39	

- the rate of formation of superoxyde anion radicals,
- the composition and antioxydizing activity of lipids of the above mentioned membranes
- the sensitivity of cells, membranes, DNA, and organisms to the action of additional damaging factors.

For all those parameters, a bimodal dose-dependent effect was discovered, i.e. the effect increased at low doses, reached its (low-dose) maximum, and then decreased (in some cases, the sign of the effect changed to the opposite, or "benefit" effect), and increased again as the dose was increased.

Professor Burlakova has speculated that at the lowest experimental doses used in this research, the repair mechanism of the cells was not triggered. It became activated at the point of the low-dose maximum, providing a "benefit", until it was overwhelmed, and the damage began again to increase with the dose. This may well be the case.

However, the unexpected effects of low-dose slow-dose rate exposure to ionising radiation, can also be attributed to biological mechanisms, which are specific to the low-slow-dose conditions. Three such secondary mechanisms have been observed by scientists : the Petkau effect, monocyte depletion and deformed red blood cells.

The Petkau effect :

The Petkau effect has been discovered by Abraham Petkau at the Atomic Energy of Canada Ltd (AECL) Whitshell Nuclear Research Establishment, Manitoba, Canada in 1972. Dr. Petkau discovered that at 26 rads/minute (fast-dose rate), it required a total dose of 3,500 rads to destroy a cell membrane. However, at 0.001 rad/minute (slow-dose rate), it required only 0.7 rad to destroy the cell membrane. The mechanism at the slow-dose rate is the production of free radicals of oxygen (O_2 with a negative electrical charge), by the ionising effect of the radiation. The sparsely distributed free radicals, generated at the slow-dose rate, have a better probability of reaching and reacting with the cell membrane, than do the densely crowded free radicals, produced by fast-dose rates. These latter recombine quickly.

Moreover, the slight electrical charge of the cell membrane attracts the free radicals in the early stages of the reaction (low total dose). This is consistent with the findings of Professor Burlakova, who has studied the alterations of the membrane's lipids under the action of free radicals, with very low doses, leading to an increase in membrane's permeability, with secondary modifications of the cell's micrometabolism and nuclear division. Computer calculations have shown that the attraction weakens with greater concentrations of free radicals. The traditional radiation biologists have tested only high-dose reactions, and looked only for direct damage to the membrane by the radiation.

Monocyte depletion :

Nuclear fission produces radionuclides, which tend to be stored by humans and animals in the bone tissue. In particular, Strontium 90, Plutonium and the transuranics have this property. Stored in bone, near the stem-cells which produce the white blood cells, these radionuclides deliver a chronic low-slow-dose of radiation, which can interfere with normal blood cell production. A few less neutrophils or lymphocytes (the white blood cells which are most numerous and are usually "counted" by the radiophysicist) are not noticeable.

In the normal adult, there are about 7,780 white cells per microlitre of blood. Of these, about 4,300 are neutrophils and 2,710 are lymphocytes. Only 500 are monocytes. If for example, stem cells in the bone marrow are destroyed, so as to reduce total white blood count by 400 cells per microlitre, due to the slow irradiation by radionuclides stored in the bone, this would represent a depletion of only 5 % in total white cells, an insignificant amount. If all of the depletion was of neutrophils, this would mean a reduction of only 9.3 %, still leaving the blood count well in the normal range. The lymphocytes would also be still in the normal range, even though they were depleted by 400 cells per microlitre, or 14.8 %.

However, there would be a dramatic depletion of the monocytes by 80%. Therefore, at low doses of radiation, it is more important to observe the monocytes than to wait for an effect on the lymphocytes or neutrophils (as is now usually done). The effects of serious reduction in monocytes are :

- Iron deficient anemia, since it is the monocytes which recycle about 37 - 40 % of the iron in the red blood cells when they die.

- Depressed cellular immune system, since the monocyte secrete the substance which activates the lymphocyte immune system.

Deformed red blood cells :

Dr. Les Simpson, of New Zealand, has identified deformed red blood cells he observed under an electron microscope, as causing symptoms ranging from severe fatigue to brain dysfunction, leading to short-term memory loss. He has identified such cells in elevated number in chronic fatigue patients, and speculated that, because of their bloated or swollen shape, they are obstructing the tiny capillaries, thus depriving muscles and the brain of adequate oxygen and nutrients. The chronic fatigue syndrome has been observed both at Hiroshima and Nagasaki, called "Bura-Bura" disease, and at Chernobyl.

Not generally recognised :

In the official approach to radiobiology, only direct damage to DNA has been recognised as "of concern", and only high-dose and fast-dose rate experiments or observations have been accepted. In fact, the "common wisdom" declares that effects of low doses and slow-dose rates cannot be detected, but must be extrapolated from the officially accepted high-dose and fast-dose rate studies.

This approach is rejected by the work of Professor Burlakova and the other research above noted.

The President :

Thank you, Dr. Bertell.

I now call on Professor Kryshanovskaya from Kiev.

Professor Ludmilla Kryshanovskaya :

Ladies and Gentlemen, dear Judges,

I am very happy to testify before this Tribunal. I want to thank Ms. Susan Boos, Dr. Bertell and Dr. Nidecker, who allowed me to be here today. I am working at the Neurological Institute in Kiev, that was ranked the second in importance in the former Soviet Union. Ukraine is a country

123

of unique geographical position, a mild climate, a country with one third of the world's black soils, with a great history, culture and with nice people.

What happened in Chernobyl on April 26, 1986, is the worst catastrophe in the history of nuclear power, and the highest radioactive contamination of the environment ever recorded. The accident happened on Friday night. We were given no official explanation whatsoever. When we listened to the Voice of America and the BBC, we did not believe them. We thought that this was impossible in our country, but the impossible happened.

We now know that other accidents had happened before. In those times, even small accidents were kept secret : unpleasant social effects were hidden from the public eyes. The authorities made no declaration before May 1st, because they did not want to cancel the ceremonies and Labour Day Parades.

This disaster has cut our lives into two parts : before and after Chernobyl.

Chernobyl is situated 65 miles (110 km) from Kiev. The explosion of the Chernobyl reactor had and continues to have great political, social and public health consequences. Many people still suffer from the consequences of the catastrophe. Their lives have been changed because of the radioactivity, and they continue to suffer from it, because of the radioactive contamination of their environment. They are afraid of seing their children falling ill.

The inhabitants of the villages do not believe in their political authorities anymore. They would like to undertake their own measures, find themselves their own level of contamination.

The task of cleaning up the 30 km zone was left to 800,000 workers, called liquidators, brought in from different regions of the former Soviet Union. They were also involved in working in the hot zone on very short shifts. Most of them were exposed to radiation for an average of two months, often without proper safety equipment or radiation recording badges. As most of them didn't know the truth about the level of radiation, it wasn't so stressful to work there.

According to the Minister of Health, in 1993, more than half of the territory of Ukraine was affected by Chernobyl.

About 2.8 million people are now living on the contaminated territory.

From 1990 to 1993, the health status of the population indicated that only 28-32 percent among the adult population were healthy, and 27-30 percent of the children.

The number of healthy persons has decreased. There is a strong tendency towards the increase of chronic, non-specific diseases among the population : gastro-intestinal, respiratory, cardio-vascular diseases, cancer. One of the most tragic consequences is the increase of thyroid cancer among children.

I will mainly talk about mental and psychological problems. In 1993, the book "Chernobyl : What Can We Learn?" was published in the United States. This book is about the details of acute radiation syndromes, thyroid disorders and about the psychological problems that appeared in liquidators.

When the dose of radiation reaches 40-50 rems, it can cause all kinds of mental disorder.

At present, many of the liquidators engaged in combating the Chernobyl disaster consequences, are being diagnosed as having non-psychotic disorders. The classification of these disorders is disputable, and is the subject of debate among psychiatrists, neurologists and psychologists.

Before 1991, all the data was kept a secret. Patients were sent to special hospitals. The most popular diagnosis was "vegetative dystonia". It was a vague definition, which included a great variety of disorders. Not all the physicians agreed with this diagnosis.

After 1991, they began to publish some articles and materials on the mental disorders affecting the liquidators of the Chernobyl disaster. There were three different opinions :

- The first one was that most of these disorders were functional : vegetative dystonia, neurotic disorders, post-traumatic stress disorders, radiophobia, stress, distress and psychosomatic disorders.

- The second one was that the patient suffered from organic mental disorders.

- The third that some patients had post-traumatic stress disorders, pseudo-neurotic syndromes, psychosomatic disorders, somatisation disorders, hypochondria, anxiety disorders, different depressive syndromes and organic mental disorders.

Until today, there is no clear criteria for the diagnosis of these disorders. It depends on the psychological or neurological school you belong to.

In 1990, the Ukrainian Institute for Social and Forensic Psychiatry began to study the consequences of the Chernobyl disaster in the people who had taken part on the liquidation.

The psychological and mental status of 380 liquidators were assessed, both clinically and psychologically. The investigations began 4 and more years after the catastrophe. All of the patients were treated in a special hospital, opened after the Chernobyl disaster. Most of our patients were sent by general physicians to our psychiatric consultations, for psychological and psychiatric problems. The aim of our study was to determine the clinical and psychological aspects of non-psychotic mental disorders, related to the Chernobyl disaster.

A special questionnaire and psychological tests were developed to obtain the information. We looked at the time of the beginning of the illness in patients having received a high level of radiation. The dose received by our patients depends on the time when they began their work in the contaminated area and of its duration. The first signs of disorders appeared at the end of 1986 among 55 % of our patients. It took about 1.5, sometimes 2 years and more, for those disorders to evolve.

The average age of our patients was 30-45 years at that time. Most them had similar multiple complaints : headache, dizziness, fatigue or chronic tiredness, poor concentration and lack of attention, memory loss, irritability, sometimes anger, mood swings, anxiety, exhaustion after physical and mental activities, high blood pressure, respiratory disregulation, feelings of hopelessness and worthlessness, and lack of libido. They had also a high sensitivity to loud noises, bright light and high temperatures.

The overall symptoms of these patients were so similar, that we called this syndrome : "Cerebrasthenic post-Chernobyl Syndrome". In some cases the cerebrasthenic syndrome developed into an encephalopathic syndrome.

The pathological changes in these cases included auto-immune, neuro-immune reactions, biochemical and EEG changes. At the same time, most of our patients suffered from various somatic diseases.

The results of psychological examination of those patients indicated poor attention, lack of concentration and memory loss, mental exhaustion, reduction of mental ability, and inability of attention. 70 % of patients had a very high level of anxiety. Some patients couldn't even remember their phone numbers, or what they just had read in the newspaper. Sometimes they did not remember where they were going.

More than 80 percent had changes in their character, and 90 percent had low levels of self-esteem and self-evaluation.

At our Institute, we saw many patients, and we realised that it was very difficult, and sometimes impossible, to sort out all these symptoms. Psycho-organic syndromes can evolve in three stages :

- The first is mild, with asthenia or cerebrasthenia, reduction of emotional ability, decrease of mental and physical working ability, changes in mood, poor attention, lack of concentration and memory impairment.

- The second stage is moderate, which includes all of the first stage, plus personality changes, irritability, dysphasia, periods of anger and psychotic-like states.

- The third one is severe, with important aggravation of the symptoms of the first and second stages, plus instability, intellectual and cognitive disorders.

Clinical and psychological examinations allowed us to describe a specific "post-Chernobyl Cerebrasthenic Syndrome" as the first stage of organic mental disorders. This syndrome is one of the typical diseases which appeared after the Chernobyl disaster.

Today, the diagnosis, the prevention and the treatment of neuropsychiatric syndromes, especially those related to low doses of radiation and to acute radiation sickness, are of great interest for neurologists and psychiatrists. They need to be further analysed and studied. We need to investigate the long term evolution of these disorders, together with scientists of different countries.

The investigation of mental and neurological disorders is a

very, very important problem. It is not caused by stress, it is caused by the influence of various doses of radiation on the brain. I would like to make it clear once more, that when we are talking about mental and psychological problems, we do not mean stress, neither distress, nor psychosomatic disorders, we mean all these psychological changes and mental problems we are recording.

Without international co-operation, and support for joint projects, we can't solve this important problem. Without the international help, it will be very difficult for us to prove the real existence of all these changes, and to find objective methods to investigate them.

The President :

Thank you very much, Professor Kryshanovskaya.
I now give the floor to Professor Titov from Minsk.

Professor Leonid Titov

In our Institute in Minsk, we examined approximately 10,000 children from Belarus, between 1986 and 1995. We looked at various proteins, which have a role in the immune system of children.

Here are our results for this period. In 4,300 children we found a variation in the number of T-lymphocytes. The abnormal findings increase in the highly contaminated zones, when compared to the controls. We found a similar result with B-lymphocytes and for immunoglobulines in the contaminated zones :

From the 26 April on, we saw a fall in the number of the T- and B-lymphocytes (fig. 39), which reached its lowest point 40 days after the disaster. Then we saw a return to normal, with a new decrease about 90 days after the disaster, with a slower return to a somewhat lower norm. T-lymphocytes showed several alterations.

As to immunoglobulines, the curve is similar. After a decrease of their concentration, the curve returns to a lower norm (fig. 40).

We found a very interesting link between radiation dose (low doses) and the alterations of the immune system, especially the antibodies (fig. 41) : We find a non-linear correlation when increasing from very low doses, which confirms the work of Professor Burlakova.

It is very important to find out what is happening with the immune system of children living in very contaminated zones. We studied children from zones contaminated by different levels of Cs 137. Between 19 and 27 Curie/square kilometre, the number of T-lymphocytes has a tendency to decrease.

The modification of these parameters depends on the absorbed Cs 137 dose. The children with a reduced IgG (gamma-globulins), pointing to a reduced reaction of their immune system, have high doses of Cs 137 in their organism. Cs 137 uptake in the organism induces changes in the immune system and leads to a reduction of IgG.

Long-term studies are crucial. We have comparative dates for 1986 and 1994. In 1986, there were changes, with a return to sub-normality. A high proportion of children have a reduced lymphocyte count. The same is true for the T-lymphocytes as compared to the control group. For the T-lymphocytes supressors, there is a similar situation : decrease of the T-helpers which increase the defence mechanisms against various infections, and important increase of T-lymphocytes suppressors, which reduce these defence mechanisms.

We found a 4-fold increase of the TNF factor in the blood of children living in a very contaminated area, as compared to the controls.

We also found an increase in the number of circulating auto-antibodies in the blood of those children : These are very complex, very pathogenic proteins, which induce several auto-immune disorders in various organs.

A very similar situation of the auto-immunology exists in children living in contaminated zones : increase of auto-antibodies, of rheumatic diseases etc.

The absorption of Cs 137 and other radionuclides by children can influence the development of the stem-cells in the bone-marrow, with very important alterations of the immune system. We have to look much closer at the immune system, at its alterations, and the dose-related modifications. We must also establish a register of the immunological disorders.

In conclusion, the immune system of children has been impaired after the catastrophe of Chernobyl : we find various disorders of the immune system in children and adults. During the 10 years since the catastrophe, people have incorporated Cs 137 and other radionuclides which accumulate in their organism.

I wish to all the inhabitants of our planet a good functioning of their immune system and of their mind.

The President :

Thank you very much, Professor Titov.

I now give the floor to Professor Gres, from Minsk.

Professor Nika Gres :

I want to give you some information about a very specific ecological situation, which we discovered in the southern parts of Belarus (the Pripyat marshes), after the Chernobyl catastrophe, and which has never been mentioned.

You know the special procedures that were maintained in the contaminated zone, according to the levels of contamination, the limit being 5 Curie per square kilometre.

We discovered a geological specificity in some territories where the radiation is less than 5 Curie/km. In territories with low density of Cs 137 contamination, but where the soil is very acidic, we observed that the rate of transmigration in the food-chain is extremely high, from 2 to 15 times higher than in other regions. This is due to the specific geological situation. So the level of soil contamination is very low, but because of the high speed of transmigration, all the food is contaminated with a high level of radionuclides.

The children are at high risks. We compared 1,650 children having received doses 3 or 5 times higher than control children. And what is the most important is that 95 to 96 percent of this radioactivity comes through internal contamination (fig. 25). It is increasing year after year. Every child has a small Chernobyl reactor inside it, inside its digestive system. So according to the special equipment Professor Nesterenko has already been speaking of, we checked the level of contamination of the children. They have internal exposures up to 1,190 Becquerel/kg weight.

The tragedy is not limited to these factors. We discovered that the children showed a high level of lead. In the control group it is 0.06 ppm, which is standard. The level we discovered among children living in contaminated areas was 0.12 ppm, and the level of lead among children suffering from sicknesses of the digestive system was 0.18 up to 0.20 ppm (ports pro mille).

We are certain, and we want to underline this, that this lead is connected with Chernobyl, it is not industrial lead, because all the children live in small villages, there are no plants, no factories, just roads. We know that in the first days after the Chernobyl disaster, they poured lead into the burning reactor in order to stop the fire. They poured lead down from helicopters, the temperature was 3,000° at this time and the lead was mixed with Cesium 137 and vaporised. Now we discover it in children.

Very recently we discovered a third aggravating factor. Usually in villages they use water from the water table, and all this water has levels of nitrates 2 or 3 times higher than standard. These three factors, lead plus nitrates, plus Cesium 137 come through food and water. That is why the digestive system is at a very high risk, because it accumulates all these three factors.

We used following the methods for our monitoring : 298 children constituted the main group, 153 children were in the control group. They all lived in the same socio-economic conditions, but there was a difference in the ecological situation. The 298 children lived under the influence of these 3 combined factors, and the control group lived in a territory where the radioactivity was standard. There was no problem of lead there, and the nitrates in the drinking water were near normal. The age of the children was 10-17.

About 80 percent of the 298 children living in a contaminated territory have all kinds of complications concerning the digestive system (fig. 26).

1. We studied the Helicobacter infections, which are in the centre of attention because there is evidence that Helicobacter is provoking stomach cancers. According to the scientific literature in the Eastern countries, 35 % of the affected people have this infection. 85 % of the children with chronic digestive illnesses have Helicobacter pylori. Only 5 % of the healthy children have them. 40 % of all the children screened suffer from this infection (controls and study group).

2. The atrophy of the digestive mucosa is found in 16 % of the children in the contaminated area and only 2 % in the control group.

3. The incidence of intestinal metaplasia, with changes in the digestive cells is 10 % in the children living in contaminated areas, and only in 2 % in the controls.

36.8 % of the children, who show trophic problems in their digestive system (against 8 % of the controls), have the highest level of these three factors : lead, Cesium 137 and nitrates.

These illnesses, atrophy of digestive system, and a certain degree of metaplasia of the stomach mucosa, are common in the old age. Presently, our children present the features of old people (fig. 27).

In conclusion, the combination of Helicobacter pylori infections and of atrophies and metaplasia, go together with a very high risk of digestive cancer. The very high incidence of these three factors, predict a future surge of digestive cancers in this population. It will be like a second Chernobyl, which will start when these children will be 20-25 year old.

The President :

Thank you, Professor Gres.

I now give the floor to Professor Jay Gould

Professor Jay Gould :

I want to present to the Tribunal my latest book, written with Dr. Mangano : "The Enemy Within", where we present the risks of living near nuclear power plants. In the United States, the levels of radiation measured in May 1986 were far below those encountered by the residents of Ukraine and Belarus. However we have such good statistics on both health variables and radiation levels in the US, that it is possible for us to find correlation.

We found for example, that the high rate of thyroid cancer, experienced by children and adults in Belarus and Ukrain, were also duplicated in the US. This chart depicts the incidence of thyroid cancer in the US, as recorded by the Connecticut Tumour Registry, which is the oldest and best in the world, having started in 1935.

During the period 1935-1944, which is pre-nuclear, the trend of the thyroid cancer rate was very low, less than one in a million cases, it was even declining.

The nuclear age really began in 1944, according to the US Department of Energy (DoE), which recently revealed some data, showing that in 1944 and 1945, in the haste to produce Plutonium for the first atomic bombs, the Hanford nuclear plant released enormous amounts of radioactive Iodine, of the magnitude of the Chernobyl explosion. The exact figure is very amazing, it has never been reported in any newspaper : Three years ago, the DoE revealed that in 1945, Hanford released something in the order of 550,000 Curie of radioactive Iodine.

Nowadays, we measure radioactive Iodine in milk and water in terms of picoCurie, where a picoCurie is a trillionth of a Curie. The DOE is now admitting that in 1945, the American population was unwittingly exposed to a exposure of over 4 billion picoCurie *per capita*.

This explains why you see in this chart a tremendous increase in the rate of thyroid cancer in 1945. It increased 5 fold since 1945. (Fig. 43).You see that every peak came about 5 years after a large insult, including the peak five years after Chernobyl in 1991.

Several states have very good tumour registers. Every month, the Environment Protection Agency (EPA), measures the level of radioactive Iodine in about 60 cities. In those states and areas with heavy rainfall, high levels of radioactive Iodine in the milk have been measured (fig. 41).

In May and June of 1986, when the Chernobyl radiation hit the United States, there were heavy rainfall levels in the North/West, where we found a significant increase in not only the thyroid cancer rate in the 2 following years, 1986 to 1987 (fig 42), but also, and this is quite remarkable, in the rate of new-born hypothyroidism.

Since the Three Mile Island accident in 1979, every State Department of Health in the US, has been measuring the percentage of hypothyroid cases in new-born in all live births. They know that starting 1979, a remarkable increase has been observed. Hypothyroidism is a very rare condition, but it has been rising very rapidly since 1985-86, then somewhat levelled off in 1991 and 1992. This extraordinary epidemiological increase testifies at least to

133

the fact that the radioactive Iodine, which came in with Chernobyl, must have been a factor.

This really validates what Professor Burlakova told us about the effects of low doses. We have divided the states into five regions, according to the degree of exposure to rainfall and radioactive Iodine. The curve shows no linear response, but what is a downward concave, or logarithmic response, where the risk is greatest at the lowest level.

We asked ourselves why is the hypothyroidism still increasing, when radioactive Iodine has only a half-life of 8 days ? A very good question, which we think can be answered possibly by some of the suggestions made by Professor Burlakova. We think that what happened, and this is a theory, but it's one that has to be investigated, particularly with the experience in Ukraine and Belarus, was that along with the radioactive Iodine there was Strontium 90, and in fact we measure it : The levels of Strontium 90 and Iodine found in the milk in the United States, were between 1 and 3 picoCurie per litre, which we regard as very low. But the lethal affects of low-level radiation are really quite high.

Strontium 90 is bone-seeking, which means that it is also bad for the immune response, which is the basis of all the problems that we are talking about. Strontium 90 also has a daughter radio-isotope which concentrates itself in the pituitary gland, which might have a secondary affect on hypothyroidism. In other words, pregnant woman ingest Strontium 90, which, long after the Iodine has decayed, will have an effect on the pituitary gland, with a feed-back relationship on other immune-deficiency diseases.

This might be an explanation for what is a very puzzling fact, that not only the hypothyroidism continues to increase, but also the percentage of low birth-weights is still going up as Dr. Bertell pointed out in her paper. The percentage of underweight babies is one of the most sensitive indicators of radiation-induced immune deficiency, and that is still going up in the United States.

The rate of premature births, which is related to low birth-weight rates, is increasing very rapidly, taking off in 1992. These are indicators that the United States shares with the former Soviet Union : the health effects are not only due to the Chernobyl radiation, but to all the radiation that came before Chernobyl. Both countries have been addicted to the use of nuclear power, and emissions from those stations have contributed greatly to the health effects we describe in our book.

We have studied the official data on the age-related breast cancer mortality figures, for every County in the United States since 1950. These datas carefully collected by the National Cancer Institute, have never been published before. Thanks to our computer, we are now in a position to do our own age adjustments. We presented a series of maps around each of the 60 civilian and military nuclear reactors in the US. Out of the 60, 55 have within a range of 50 to 100 miles, statistically significantly higher risks of breast cancer mortality. The United States is a very large country, but in large patches of area, in every county that is within a 50-100 mile radius of a reactor, women have a much higher risk of dying of breast cancer, and there is also an increase of other immune-deficiency problems, like low birth-weight and also AIDS, an acquired immune deficiency disease.

We believe, and we would like to propose this to the Judges, that we can trace to the low-level radiation released from the onset of the nuclear age, the beginning of most of the health problems that now besiege not only the former Soviet Union, but the United States too.

In the United States, we have made an arrangement to have our book distributed by Greenpeace and by the Methodist Church, so that for every copy they sell to their members, the profit margin goes to their own organisation. We would like to make that arrangement available here in Europe too. Perhaps the Commission might undertake to make it available to any non-profit organisation in Europe, who would take on the job of translating and distributing this book. We believe it tells a story, not only about the Soviet Union, but what is worrying, about all the countries that were subjected to radiation from the onset of the nuclear age.

The President :

Thank you very much for this book.

Is according to you all nuclear energy dangerous?

Professor Jay Gould :

Routine radioactive emissions are dangerous, because they are a major source of low-level radiation. High levels would come from large accidents. I would like to come back on the studies undertaken many years ago by Dr. Abraham Petkau, a Canadian atomic physicist. He discovered that the dose response to radiation is logarithmic, which is to say concave downwards, so that the risk is greater with low levels of radiation.

The damage to the immune response, caused by low-level radiation, can, to some extent be combated by measures taken to boost the immune system : anti-oxydants, vitamin C, vitamin E. The biochemical mechanism by which the damage is done to the immune system, is different from the damage done to the DNA, that comes from high levels of radiation. At low-level radiation, you have among other mechanisms, the formation of free radicals, as was also shown by Professor Burlakova, which can be negated by anti-oxydants like vitamin C and vitamin E. However, the only way to really deal with the problem of low-level radiation is to stop as soon as possible the operation of every nuclear reactor in the world.

On page 79 of the book I presented to the Judges, we find a very important table, which will answer your question. One of the most sensitive indicators of radiation damage, as I said before, is the percentage of live births under 2,500 grams. In the United States, the low birth-weight percentage began to rise in 1945. In New York State for example, it grows from about 6 % to about 9 % in 1965. It began to improve with the cessation of underground testing, but in the late 70's, particularly after the Three Mile Island accident, it started going up again and it's still going up.

We found that the increase of the percentage of babies with a low birth-weight, is an indicator of the radiation-induced damage to the immune response. For example, we found that the 40 or 50 % rise in the low birth-rate percentage, from 1945 to 1965, was duplicated thereafter in the health of the baby-boom generation. When the baby-boom generation reached the age of 18, in 1963 in the US, an inexplicable drop in the intellectual performances and SAT scores at examinations were observed, which went on for 20 years, exactly duplicating the previous increase in the low birth-weight percentage.

My colleague, Dr Sternglass, was the first to realise that this was affecting the SAT scores, and he has established that there are parallel socio-economic anomalies that accompany this. For example, starting in 1970, the baby-boom generation began a 20 year period, in which they dropped out of the labour force, they became socially unproductive. Starting in 1980, when they reached the age of 35, we have a period where immune-deficiency diseases such as AIDS and increasing degrees of breast cancers among young women began to appear. This is another indication of an original insult, that came from the period of above-ground testing, which, according to the National Defence Council, represented the equivalent of 40,000 Hiroshima bombs explosions. That's the kind of radiation exposure that the children of the US and the USSR have been exposed to.

We were able to show, that in each of the nuclear countries, in the 80's, you could measure the degree of immune-system damage to the baby-boom generation, by simply showing what percentage of total deaths they accounted for in the year 1983, and then in 1988. In all the nuclear countries, that percentage went up, whereas from 1900 to 1980, the percentage contributed to all deaths by the 25-44 year group had been decreasing. So for 80 years, this group, that was the healthiest group in the labour force, was improving their health, and then, from 1983 to 1988, in the nuclear countries, their death-rate suddenly went up.

One of the greatest ironies of all is that the only countries that did not suffer from that deterioration in the baby-boom generations mortality, are Japan and Germany, precisely because they lost World War 2. They were precluded from exposing their progeny to the fission products from the manufacturing and testing of nuclear bombs. You can say in a way that having lost World War 2, they won, in effect, World War 3.

The President :

On what basis did you get these percentages, these statistics?

Professor Jay Gould :

All the statistics come from the Demographic Year Books of the United Nations, which shows how many people died each year by age group. If you take the percentage of all deaths in 1983 and 1988 contributed by the age group 25-44, (which represents the baby-boom generation), you find that in the US that percentage increased by 18 %, in France by 15 %, in the UK by 8 %, and that it had declined in Germany and Japan. In other words, according to the UN figures, the baby-boom generations of Japan and Germany actually had their mortality improved.

Many countries fall in-between, because even if you don't have nuclear reactors, as in the case of Norway, you are influenced by the reactors in the United Kingdom, by Sellafield. In fact, at a conference several years ago, Norway said that they had found that, because of the mountain range in the middle of Norway, the children on the Western side of the mountain range had a lower scholastic score than children on the Eastern side, because they were exposed to radiation from the Sellafield reactors. Austria has no reactors, but Switzerland has, and both suffer from the reactors in France. It's a very unfair situation, which indicates again, that the first priority for the countries of the world, is to eliminate nuclear reactors, whether military or civilian.

The President :

I thank you, Professor Gould.

Now we come to question time. The Tribunal has listen to very technical testimonies and we will need some explanations.

I give the floor to Professor Schmitz-Feuerhake.

Professor Inge Schmitz-Feuerhake :

My name is Inge Schmitz-Feuerhake. I am a physicist, working at the University of Bremen in Germany. I have been working for many years in the field of dosimetry and the effects of low doses.

At present we investigate a tremendous, exceptional leukemia increase in the proximity of a German nuclear power plant : Krümmel.

The official arguments are well known, they say that low-dose radiation, delivered by nuclear power plants in normal operation are not able to cause such important effects. We were able to show chromosome aberrations in the people living there, and we know now, from certain contamination which were measured in the vicinity, that there was an exposure to short lived isotopes, and that there was an exposure far above legal limits, even though the supervising ministry attested normal operation.

The owners of these facilities should be controlled, but a heavy pressure is exerted on those people who want to elucidate the effects of radioactive releases. In Germany, you can't get colleagues from the universities to support you in such investigations. The mainstream research is clearly directed along the line of the promotion of nuclear power, even though the opinion-polls in Germany show that more than half the people are opposed to nuclear power. No official funds or federal research moneys are given, of course, to so-called "people who are not objective". They say that as an anti-nuclear researcher, you are not objective.

The consequence is that you are not able to publish your results in international journals, because the peers always declare that you are not serious. This is nothing new. It is the experience of many of us, and Dr. Bertell knows this, and this was the motivation for founding a critical scientific journal, "International Perspectives in Public Health".

What we have heard today from our colleagues from Russia, Ukraine and Belarus, is that chronic low-dose exposure is much more harmful than it is thought in the official mainstream thinking. For decades, they have told us that the most dangerous exposure had been that of Hiroshima and Nagasaki, where you had one single massive dose-rate event, and they said that chronic exposure has no harmful consequences. Official experts recognise now that a chronic exposure to low doses can cause cancers. But they also say that the lesson of the Japanese experience show that there will only be a very small number of cancers, practically negligible.

What we have to learn now is what are the effects, we must listen to those scientists who have always been critical in this field, and who didn't believe the things that were put down in the books and the lessons. Even for us, what we have heard here is very new evidence. We have underestimated the consequences of events such as occurred at Chernobyl. Other events were also underestimated, Three Mile Island is an example, also the consequences of the fallout of all the nuclear explosions, which have to this day not been correctly quantified, and so on. This is my comment inspired by the testimonies heard today.

The President :

Thank you very much, Professor Schmitz-Feuerhake.

I now give the floor to Dr. Nidecker.

Dr. Andreas Nidecker :

I represent a physician's organisation, called the International Physicians for the Prevention of Nuclear War (IPPNW). This is an old organisation, founded in the United States in the 60's as Physicians for Social Responsibility (PSR), and internationalised in the early 80's.

The traditional focus of our organisation has been nuclear proliferation, nuclear war. Some affiliates, particularly in Europe, in Germany and in Switzerland, however, have considered the target of nuclear power in general to be very important.

In Switzerland, the reason for that was a 25 or 20 year old political discussion about what to do about nuclear power. This discussion has been very lively for all this time, and IPPNW was asked early on to take sides, and decide what to do.

Switzerland presently observes a 10 year moratorium, where no decisions about nuclear power can be made in our country. We, physicians in Switzerland, (there are about 1200 doctors in our country in our affiliate), considered it essential to throw in the weight and the credibility of our medical profession. I think that it is very important to realise that it is our credibility and weight that can add to the general decision-making processes, as regards the future of nuclear power.

Nowadays, governments sometimes are not trustworthy, and even if they were, they are frequently out of money. People are not organised, and they are dependent, and many times not knowledgeable. Political parties are unimaginative and unable to incite enthusiasms.

The NGOs are independent, they can have new ideas and can act quickly. Therefore, I believe that it is crucial that this small group, gathered in this room, have a strong impact on the Judge's Verdict.

I consider however that it is important to leave open a line of dialogue with the promoters of nuclear energy. I assume that we can call them gangsters only in this circle, and even if they may be gangsters, I think that this is not the way to talk publicly, because we immediately loose the ability to talk to them. I think it is very important that we discuss with persons who believe, maybe because of poor information or of confined vision, that nuclear energy is a real possibility.

Time works for us, there is a mountain of evidence on the damages, as we have heard during the IAEA Conference this week. There is a split among the promoters of nuclear power. Not everybody who was present at the IAEA Conference was really wholeheartedly supportive of it. Towards the end of the Conference, people from Ukraine and Belarus stood up, and some of them were able to bring in the critique.

Secondly, the costs are increasing with every increasing safety measures to be taken, it has become uneconomical to run nuclear power plants today. It's much cheaper to use energy-efficiency measures.

I would encourage you all to read the book by Amory Lovins and Ernst von Weizsäcker, "Factor Four", which gives many completely new ideas about the energy future, and this is one message I would like to give to the Tribunal. We cannot just talk about the damage inflicted by nuclear power plants, without addressing the alternative issues.

I think it is very important that the Judges point, in their Verdict, towards the alternatives to nuclear power, and that their Judgement does not just confine itself to the damage that has been inflicted, which is great and will increase.

Many politicians, many academics in Eastern European countries, in Russia, do not know that there exist alternatives, yet in Germany and in Switzerland, we see that other ways are possible. When you read a book like "Factor Four", a whole new world opens up in the world of energy sources.

We also need, from this panel, to try to influence the credit policies of financial institutions like the World Bank. They should start giving credits for alternatives to nuclear power, not just money for refurbishing the old nuclear reactors. The lending policies of these financial bodies should be influenced.

I would like to explain why, as a radiologist, I am critical about nuclear energy, even though I use radiation in a diagnostic way. I also perform diagnostic studies in nuclear medicine, but when I inject radioactive substances into the body of a patient, this patient already has their own risk from their disease. A small amount of radiation, for diagnostic use, in a sick person, is worth taking the risk. Whereas if you irradiate whole countries, and millions of people are contaminated without any possibility to defend themselves, I think that is a quite different matter. I think that even as a radiologist, you can be very critical of nuclear energy.

I would like to finish up by citing a reference from Hengst "A Time Bomb Radioactivity", which in turn cites the Viennese philosopher Günter Anders, who died a few years ago. He said "Morituri of all countries, unite!" If we continue with nuclear power, this is what we would be, "morituri", we will die.

There is another reference by Hesselstein, of the United States Nuclear Regulatory Commission (NRC), in the aftermath of Chernobyl. He said the following, "Given the present levels of safety being achieved by the operating nuclear power plants in this country, we can expect to see a core meltdown accident within the next 20 years, and it is possible that such an accident could result in off-site releases of radioactivity, that are as large or larger than releases estimated to have occurred at Chernobyl. We have a very important message to give and a high responsibility".

Thank you for having allowed me to speak.

The President :

Thank you very much, Dr. Nidecker.

I now give the floor to Professor Acquilla.

Professor Sushma Acquilla :

Thank you for the opportunity to talk to you. I am lecturing in public health at the University of Newcastle-on-Tyne. For the last 3 years, my department and my colleagues have developed some interest about environmental factors and their effects on health. I am also member of the International Medical Commission on Bhopal.

What I would like to say is, having heard about all these effects, that the biggest problem for the scientists is to convince the public opinion, and the politicians, of the effect of any exposure of radioactivity to the health.

It is quite easy to demonstrate the effect of an acute exposure, because you deal with a quite large dose, you see immediately some consequences, you see a large amount of people being affected, a large amount of people dying, and that's quite easy to explain.

When you talk about low-level pollution, be that radiological or any other pollution, by the time you get statistically significant results, it may take you 15, 20, 30, 40 years, by which time it is too late for any scientific community to raise their voice.

The other problem which has been mentioned by previous speakers, is the publication bias. If you try to publish results, saying that this particular pollution is causing diseases, they may not like to accept it, because such results are not politically acceptable.

The third problem is that even if we find an excess of disease in the affected or exposed population, the difficulty to assign the effects to the exposure. Most of the time, people living in the nearby area, in the industrial area, are poor, and diseases among them are quite common. It may prove very difficult to separate out the diseases of poverty from the diseases of exposure to any pollutant. How much do you attribute to their poverty and how much do you attribute to the actual exposure? The best way would be if everybody carried some kind of dosimeter, which tells how much exposure they've had. If they develop more diseases than those who have not been exposed, then we can tell, but that's not possible in real life. I think that one important thing is to develop alternative means of measuring exposure.

For the people who live in places like Chernobyl, and have been affected, I feel that they have had research done on them, over and over, and over, and over again. Different experts groups come, and do research on them, which they never see the results of. First of all, this research does not get published, but even if it would not necessarily be in an academic journal, it would not get to the victims anyway.

The important thing to say here is, that the information needs to be communicated to the people who are being affected, so that they can unite in pressure groups, work with NGOs, and take actions. We have already heard that politicians won't take such actions because it turns against them.

The other thing is, that if you are going to places like Sellafield, and speak to people who are employed in Sellafield, to them their job is more important. We have also to tell them how dangerous their job is.

We should try to put dangerous industries somewhere else, and protect workers within it, so that it still gives employment, and move the residential areas away from the industry. If that was possible, it is something that could be done.

The nuclear industry itself is interesting for the developing world, because it is a cheap source of energy. The problem there would be that the standards of safety that are applied in the western world would not be applied. That means that if you can expect to have an accident in the developed world once in every 30 or 40 years, this might happen every 10 years in the developing world, because the safety would be that lax, and nobody would be following the instructions. At the end of the day, we have Bhopal, Chernobyl, and who gets blamed for it? It's either a non-named head of a transnational firm, or the workers who didn't follow correctly the instructions.

Finally, with an industry like this, you must inform the people in the surrounding areas what their risks are in terms of living in its vicinity. There is no point in waiting for a disaster to happen, because if you wait for a disaster, the people living in the affected area get some kind of stigma, they loose the value of their houses, so even if they want to move, they cannot sell their houses. Once a disaster has happened, nobody would move into the area, so the government must take the forceful action of moving them from the affected area to a clean area.

Thank you very much for listening to me.

Thank you very much, Professor Acquilla.

We will now hear the questions from the Jury.

Judge Freda Meissner-Blau :

I have a question for Dr. Nidecker. We know we should insist on the alternatives, but I am encountering more and more difficulty in trying to convince people. Perhaps you have an idea on how to handle this. We tell our friends in the Czech Republic, in Slovakia, that they should struggle for alternative energies. They say in a very justified way : "You show us how you get your government to install on a big scale wind and solar energy". It is terribly difficult to expect from another country, which has been offered nuclear energy, to use alternatives.

The other question to Professor Acquilla is, do you believe that it is really a solution to follow the temptation, and continue to work for the nuclear energy ? Dr. Robert Jungk, who unfortunately died recently and wrote outstanding books on nuclear energy, proposed years ago a world-wide foundation, which would pay to help those engineers and scientists and experts who work for the nuclear sector, knowing very well that it is not a good thing, to find something interesting in the scientific field, a real alternative. Nothing has ever been done to help people to step out of it.

Dr. Andreas Nidecker :

I share your somewhat pessimistic view of the situation. I agree that we will not cure this disease from today until tomorrow. But I am certain that in my little country, there exists a strong sympathy in the population for these alternatives. The example given by Switzerland is very interesting. It is a small but rich country, which moves in the direction of alternatives. This will certainly have a impact on politicians in the eastern european countries, which will be puzzled. If the same evolution happened in Switzerland, in Austria, in Germany, it would have a major impact in the whole world.

After having read the book "Factor 4", I have the feeling that there are not many investments anymore in the nuclear field, neither in the United States nor elsewhere. Many people believe that a better use of energy, energy conservation and alternative energy sources are cheaper than nuclear energy. Why couldn't this change in the western world be shared in the East ? Our friends here from the CIS republics could use their contacts to spread this information in their countries. We must remain optimists, because, as I have already said, time works in our favour.

Professor Sushima Acquilla :

For the middle term, I totally agree with what was just said. But if you want to give jobs to those scientists, those workers, the alternatives have to be in place before we drop nuclear energy. When solar and wind energy will be in place, then we will be able to close the nuclear power plants.

The President :

Now we shall hear all the questions from the Judges, and then we will ask the experts to reply.

Judge Elmar Altvater :

I have also a question to Dr. Nidecker.

Do you really believe that the alternative energy sources will be able to replace nuclear energy without adverse effects on the social and economic development ? Day after day, progress is made in the energy sector, but when I look at the conclusions of the IAEA, they declare that nuclear energy is a progress as regards fossil energy sources, which contribute to the greenhouse effect.

The IAEA believes that we need nuclear energy, but produced in safer power plants. The Institute of Prof. von Weizsäcker has shown that alternative energy sources are not sufficient, cannot be sufficient.

What we need is a new life-style, oriented towards life, towards sustainable life. This means a change in the mode of production and consuming. Don't you think that we should be more radical, when proposing alternatives ?

My second question is to Professor Schmitz-Feuerhake. I know very well the problems facing the scientific community, because it is my own community. Don't you think that the situation has changed these last years ? Shouldn't we insist on those changes ? Would this not be the role of this Tribunal, to influence the public opinion in order to change the way of thinking of the scientific community ? I would like to know if, in your personal field, you notice recent changes in the way they discuss the consequences of the nuclear energy, in publications etc...

Judge Mitsuo Okamoto :

I have a question to Professor Schmitz-Feuerhake on the epidemiological studies in Germany after the Chernobyl catastrophe. I stayed in Germany after the catastrophe, in June and July 1986. As several areas in Berlin were contaminated, I sent a sample of clay, collected in the Western sector to a laboratory in the United States, as well as a sample collected in a graveyard in Heidelberg. They confirmed that there was the same amount of radioactivity in both samples. Therefore, it seems that the contamination has been relatively uniform in western Europe. This has not been reported by the media. They referred only to Sweden, Italy and Switzerland.

My experience with southern Germany seems to indicate that low doses were found in much larger territories.

Judge Corinne Kumar :

I have three questions.

My first question is for the scientists we listened to this morning. I would like to know if they, or colleagues, have studied the effects of radiation on women. I would like to attract the interest of the media to this problem.

My second question is for Professor Jay Gould, the author of the book : "The Enemy Within". I would like to hear more about the consequences of nuclear energy for the South. You are looking at nuclear reactors in the West, in the East. But when we think of the nuclear waste dumped by the United States and the Soviet Union, of the nuclear tests in the Pacific, of the effects of nuclear fallout in Africa, how is it really ?

My third question goes to Dr. Nidecker, who made an excellent strategic presentation. How can the alternative sources of energy be utilised in the South ?

I believe by the way that we must change the dominant model of development, the concept of a purely quantitative progress, based on the Gross National Product, a consumerist and materialistic ethic. In this framework, what are the alternatives in the energy sector ?

Judge Surendar Gadekar :

I have a question for Professor Kryshanovskaya on the psychological consequences of the Chernobyl catastrophe. Did you try to find any link with what has been called the "Bura-Bura" disease, after the bombings of Hiroshima and Nagasaki ? The symptoms you have described are very similar to what is described for the "Bura-Bura" disease. We have found similar symptoms in Rajasthan.

I have also a question for Dr. Nidecker : you have spoken of a conversion to solar and wind energy. How can this be achieved in the Third World ? As a matter of fact, we see that often polluting industries, rejected in the North, are moving to the South. Will this not also be the case for the nuclear energy ?

My last question is for Professor Aquilla, who said that persons living near nuclear power plants should be informed about the risks before an accident happens. But who will present this information ? If it is the industry managers themselves, they will say that there is no risk. I hear them constantly repeating this. How and by whom will this information be produced ?

The President :

I want now to hear your responses to the 3 Judges. After this, we will collect the questions from the remaining Judges.

Professor Inge Schmitz-Feuerhake :

Judge Okamoto has asked a question on the level of contamination in Germany following the Chernobyl catastrophe. It is true that we had an important contamination. The official dosimetry says that the average cumulated dose in the organism is 0,5 mSvt. In the South, especially in Bavaria, there has been more.

Several scientists have shown the consequences of this

148

contamination : chromosomic aberrations in Bavaria, confirmed the heavy fallout. Those data have not been published, they can be found in the "grey" literature, in reports from conferences etc.

There have been several mentions of an increase of perinatal mortality in the year after the accident, which was attributed to the contamination. The perinatal mortality has been compared in the North of Germany, where it was much lower than in the South. The increase in perinatal mortality went the same way as the contamination level.

Professor Sperling, a geneticist, found Trisomy 21 in Berlin. A campaign started against his first publication, which they said was not serious. He rechecked his findings, they are well documented, and I think that they defeat every critique. There have been some publications these last two years.

I was also asked if I had noticed changes in the way of thinking of the German scientific community ? After the Chernobyl catastrophe, more physicians decided to think for themselves, and they went public against nuclear power.

But I am disappointed, because we still are a minority, without any real influence. On the other hand, we see not only auto-censure, but outright corruption. Among our colleagues, there are some who measure something and publish something else, even if it is blatant. I am feeling very sad at this, but I continue to work for a change.

Dr. Andreas Nidecker :

I realise that while speaking of solar energy, we are somewhat leaving the main subject of this Tribunal. But I hope that my message will be put into the Verdict of our Judges, and that is that there are alternatives, and that these alternatives give us reasons for hope.

Judge Altvater mentioned the book "Faktor 4". I believe that it is a very important book. After reading it, I was even more convinced that it is the only solution we have. Humanity did without nuclear energy until 40 years ago, and it will survive without nuclear energy. I am convinced of it. Why ?

The sun is so powerful that its radiation on the surface of our planet represents a very large energy source for us. I made a little calculation. If we would put solar panels or

149

photovoltaïc cells, on only one third of the roofs which are oriented to the South in Switzerland, we could close all our nuclear power plants. If energy-saving bulbs would be used everywhere in Switzerland, the energy savings would make it possible to close the Kozlodui nuclear power plant. This is what I mean by a revolution in the energy efficiency.

Professor Sushima Acquilla :

The question of the information of the public is crucial. After several disasters, many countries modified their legislation and rules. In the United Kingdom and the United States, every hazardous plant has the obligation to inform the local authorities on the releases in the air and in the water. This information is available to the public. But the problem is, that the people who live nearby, do not know how to get this information from their local authorities. I think that the responsibility for the information of the public belongs to three groups :

- The workers of these facilities have to assess for themselves the risks entailed by their jobs. Those workers should translate this information for the community where they live.
- The NGOs form the second group. They usually succeed in securing the information held by the local authorities. Most of the time, we can trust them to share this information with the public.
- The third group is formed by the professionals, the health workers. Whenever we obtain a result in our research, our first responsibility is to spread this information towards the population concerned by our research. We are responsible for our research before the public, and the public should be informed of all the risks of contamination they are taking.

The President :

I will now ask three experts to respond to the questions posed by the Judges.

I give the floor to Professor Gould.

Professor Jay Gould :

I want to respond to the question concerning the South, but also to a question which came up several times since the beginning of this session, on the complicity of certain scientists with their governments. Finally, I would like to speak on the deep crisis which presently affects the nuclear industry in the United States.

We have 17 military reactors in the United States, all closed down. This is not because the Cold War is over, as our government wants to keep its nuclear bombs. They are closed, because the buildings have become so radioactive, that the scientific and technical personnel do not want to work there anymore. There are hundreds of thousands of unemployed workers in the nuclear industry, who can find no job without unacceptable risks. Five commercial reactors are also closed down, as their cooling pools are totally filled by used fuel rods.

I have been invited to participate in a program, where officials from the Nuclear Regulatory Committee (NRC), and experts from a nuclear power plant in Connecticut, asked the public for their support. They were obliged to close down the nuclear reactor, because there was no more room in the cooling pools for the used fuel rods. They wanted to transport those used fuel rods to Yucca Mountain, in Nevada, in what is called the National Nuclear Repository. The transport of this material however, several hundreds of thousands of tons, across the United States, the Rocky Mountains, to the future facility in Nevada, risks to cause 16 accidents per year, each of them as large as the Three Mile Island catastrophe. This is an absolutely insoluble problem, which demonstrates the ultimate reality, which is that this industry is doomed.

You find this also in recent verdicts on nuclear reactors. Every one of them has waste problems which cannot be solved. Nuclear reactors are no longer profitable. There exists nowadays a strong pressure in the United States to close down the nuclear industry, for economic reasons only. If this is the case in one of the richest countries in the world, how can this technology be proposed to the countries of the South ? Our duty is to spread this kind of information.

As to the problems facing the South, the countries of the South have been affected by heavy fallout during the atmospheric tests in the fifties and the early sixties. A high percentage of this fallout reached Africa. Dr. Sternglass studied the neonatal mortality in Zaire, and showed that during the late fifties, the heavy rains contained many radionuclides, especially Strontium 90.

Much later, the children born at this time showed a depressed immune system, which culminated with the appearance of AIDS. This remarkable fact has completely been ignored by the pro nuclear scientists. As a matter of fact, it was Andreï Sakharov himself who wrote in his Memoirs, in 1958, that it was absolutely irresponsible to conduct nuclear tests because of their health effects. He mentioned the short term and long term effects of the absorbed Strontium 90 on the immune system. The generation he was speaking of was the baby-boom generation, born at a time where the radioactive fallout was that of more than 40,000 Hiroshima bombs.

He made the terrible remark that radiation increases the mutation rate in all micro-organisms. Thus it was possible to predict that the baby-boom generation, having grown up, would have to combat mutated micro-organisms with a depressed immune system.

Some scientists believe that AIDS and other acquired immune-deficiency syndromes have appeared in the very humid regions of Central Africa, where there is no nuclear reactor, but where the population is nevertheless suffering from the effects of radioactivity.

As to the problem of women and radioactivity, I think that is a very important question. Long before Chernobyl, I noticed that in my scientific field, women published more than men. I have been invited to a conference on the health effects of radiation in Oak Ridge, where people are suffering from many cancers. The number of cancers is quite similar to the pattern in Belarus. There is a great denial of those cancers, especially in men. For us, truth lies where our purse lies. Women on the other hand are suffering from the hardship of this technology. We have to understand that women are also capable of helping to get out of this nuclear nightmare.

The President :

I thank you, Professor Gould.

I now call Professor Kryshanovskaya.

Professor Ludmilla Kryshanovskaya :

I have spoken of the liquidators of the Chernobyl disaster. In 1986, most of them were aged between 25 and 35 years.

152

They were healthy young men. We have their health records from this time. They have been exposed to various radioactive doses during their work in the hot zone. As our officials and government representatives deny that they got heavy radiation doses, we have been unable to reconstruct the real dose they received.

We have performed clinical and psychological examinations and have found the results I presented to you. I believe that all the symptoms, syndromes and complaints were related to the same cause, in our liquidators and in the Japanese victims.

As you know, the officials have always refused to acknowledge any link between those diseases and the radioactivity. They tried to put everything on the stress. For my part, I think that it would be very interesting to undertake a joint study, with Japanese colleagues, scientists, psychologists, to compare our data, because these are really very interesting data.

Similar results have been found by psychiatrists in Russia and Belarus.

The President :

Thank you very much, Professor Kryshanovskaya.

I now give the floor to Professor Burlakova.

Professor Elena Burlakova :

I would like to respond to the question of Judge Kumar. This morning, we showed to you the experimental results obtained in our Institute. In the literature, many articles are based on the same statistical data. The public health statistics I used, are taken from official publications, from the Register of the Russian Ministry of Public Health. However, the conclusions drawn by official scientists from those data are diametrically opposed to ours.

In our studies, we show the harmful effects of low doses of radiation. On the opposite, let us look at the presentation made by Professor Ramsaev at the IAEA Conference on the health effects of radiation. While we found that the dose of Cesium 137 and Strontium 90, which induces cancers of the stomach is less than 1 centiGy per year, Professor Ramsaev affirms that a dose of 100 centiGy is not dangerous, although he draws his conclusions from the same statistical data as we.

Another question is that of the genetic consequences and disturbances. It has been very interesting to see the experimental studies made by Japanese on the effects of low doses of radiation in animals : they found the same results as we did. When we compare our datas, we see that in practically all cases, troubles appear with low doses, then a process of repair sets in about 25 mSvt. We cannot detect any absence of effects with doses lower than 1 centiGy.

The President :

I thank you. I thank all the experts and witnesses who spoke and responded to the questions of the Jury in this session of the Tribunal.

We now go on to a new subject that concerns the victims of the bombings of Hiroshima and Nagasaki.

6. THE JAPANESE EXPERIENCE AT HIROSHIMA AND NAGASAKI.

Speakers :   Dr. Katsumi Furitsu, Physician,
                  Investigative Committee of Atomic Bombing
                  Victims at Hannon Chuo Hospital, Osaka,
                  Japan

                  Ms. Kazuko Yamashina, Nagasaki, Atomic
                  Survivor (Hibakusha), Chernobyl Relief
                  Group of Kansai, Japan

                  Dr. Kazue Sadamori, Pharmacist,
                  Investigative Committee of Atomic Bombing
                  Victims, Hannan Chuo Hospital, Osaka, Japan

The President :

I give the floor to Dr. Furitsu, from Japan.

Dr. Katsumi Furitsu :

I want to present here several studies, relating to my presentation to the Judges.

I thank you for allowing me to speak before this Tribunal, to speak of my experience with the victims of the nuclear bombings of Hiroshima and Nagasaki. I am a physician and I take medical care of the atomic bombing survivors, the Hibakushas as they are called. Our Investigative Committee was founded in 1985.

We demand of the Japanese Government to take responsibility towards the victims of the war, and to immediately create a National Law for the Compensation of the Victims.

Today, pronuclear groups such as the IAEA, are promoting their nuclear policy by minimising the injuries of the Chernobyl catastrophe. Their philosophy is the same as that of the ABCC (Atomic Bombing Casualty Committee), and of the RERF (Radiation Effects Research Foundation) in Hiroshima and Nagasaki.

The atomic bombs, targeted on Hiroshima and Nagasaki, have often been defined as nuclear tests, designed by the United States to develop their nuclear armament. The ABCC and the RERF, joint Japanese-US bodies, conducted all research on the atomic bombing victims until 1975. Their purpose and their methods were not defined to relieve the injuries of the atomic bombing victims, but rather to negate them, in order to promote their nuclear policy. However, those bodies are considered as national authorities, having the right to establish radiation protection standards.

The study of the victims of the Chernobyl catastrophe can bring very useful information. The first problem I would like to discuss is the increase of diseases other than cancers of the thyroid and leukemia. The atomic bombing victims were suffering long time ago, and are still suffering from many disease, which are not officially recognised as consequences of radiation.

The sufferings of the people of Chernobyl after the catastrophe can also be found among our victims. From 1985 to 1990, we studied 1,232 victims of the atomic bombings, 554 men and 678 women. Their average age was 59.5 years. 50 % of the victims had been hospitalised several times or had to go regularly to the hospital. More than 90 % of the victims were still under treatment at this time, which represents a rate 2.5 time higher than the national average rate for persons of the same age, according to the Public Health Dates of the Ministry of Health of Japan in 1986 : "Basic Life dates". Lumbago was 3.6 times more frequent, hypertension 1.7 times, eye diseases 5 times, neuralgia and myalgia 4.7 times, anemia and leukopenia 13.4 times, same tendencies for gastralgia, gastritis etc (fig. 44).

ABCC and RERF have been insisting that general diseases like anemia, certain blood diseases, and cataracts, had nothing to do with radiation, according to their studies, except some cancers and leukemia.

However, there are problems with their studies. In their statistics, they have often mixed in the control group non-exposed persons with persons exposed to radiation at a certain distance. Nevertheless, the Japanese Government utilises the results from ABCC and RERF to determine the norms and limits for the compensation of the victims. Moreover, these results have been spread widely in the whole world, and the pronuclear groups are using them to ignore any compensation claims from other radiation victims, suffering from general diseases as consequences of nuclear tests, or Chernobyl.

As they for the Chernobyl victims, the pronuclear groups refuse to acknowledge any relation between the increase of many "general diseases" and the radiation received. They insist that this increase of general diseases has nothing to do with any radiation and that it is the result of the economic and social crisis, following the collapse of the Soviet Union. They contend that the injuries caused by the radiation are less important than by the economic and social situation. They refuse to take any responsibility, and to compensate the victims of Chernobyl, who are suffering from all those injuries. Deriving from the experience of the sufferings of the victims of the bombings in Hiroshima and Nagasaki, we can never accept this attitude of the pronuclear groups.

The second question I wanted to discuss here, are subjective symptoms we often find among the atomic survivors. We call them "Genbaku Bura-Bura" disease (Genbaku means atomic bombing, Bura-Bura means lingering). Many victims complain frequently about following symptoms : tiredness, vertigo, palpitations, lumbago, back aches, shoulder and neck pains. It is impossible to find precise names for every symptom. This is why they were collectively called "Genbaku Bura Bura" disease. We think that this is an important syndrome, which should be considered as being caused by the exposure to radiation.

These health injuries have been ignored, and treated as if they were "psychological troubles", by those who minimise the health problems of the victims of the bombings. However, similar syndromes have been observed among the workers exposed to radiation in nuclear power plants in Japan, or in down-winders living in the irradiated zones near Hanford, and in the Chernobyl children. We believe that this syndrome should be considered as a common symptom, caused by radiation in all kind of radiation victims. This disease should not be ignored nor attributed to stress or psychological effects.

We have shown that patients having been exposed to higher doses, nearer to the hypocenter, suffered more than persons having been irradiated at a greater distance.

The "Genbaku Bura -Bura" disease is one of the worst factors affecting the quality of life and the working ability of the victims of the atomic bombings. But the ABCC denies any relation between this disease and the exposure to radiation.

Among the Chernobyl children, and among adult Chernobyl victims, such symptoms as fatigue, headache, vertigo are often seen. Professor Kryshanovskaya already mentioned this. But the pronuclear scientists continue to say that these symptoms are caused by the constant stress, caused by the crisis, the social and psychological stress.

In conclusion, I want to repeat that if Hiroshima and Nagasaki on one side, and Chernobyl on the other side, have their specificity, there is nevertheless a great similarity in the health injuries caused by nuclear radiation. The pronuclear groups refuse to consider that those diseases are the consequences of radiation, so they do not have to compensate the victims.

We must strengthen our critiques of this attitude of the pronuclear groups such as the IAEA. Ultimately, we have to stop their nuclear policy itself, which caused the disaster, in order to have no more Chernobyl, never. Scientists, victims and soon the whole population of the world must unite to confront the pronuclear groups.

Thank you.

The President :

Thank you, Dr. Furitsu.

I now give the floor to Ms. Yamashina, a victim of the nuclear bombing.

Ms. Kasuko Yamashina :

Dear friends who are present at this International Tribunal in Vienna!

I am Kazuko Yamashina, a Hibakusha (Atomic Bomb Survivor), who lost my parents and my brother and sister in Nagasaki. I would like to speak briefly about the misery and cruelty which radiation brought about in my life.

On August 9, 1945, when the atomic bomb was dropped over the city of Nagasaki, I was working at a distance of two kilometres from ground zero. I tried to get home after the dropping of the bomb, but the fire was too fierce for me to approach the district. So, that night I had to sleep under a bridge, which was 800 metres away from our house. This was the first night I spent alone without my parents, my brother and my sister. At that time, never did I imagine that my life would become full of sickness and poverty, which the name and the fact of being a Hibakusha would give me.

My house was located at a place situated about 350 metres from ground zero. As soon as the fire went down, I reached my house and found out that my parents were burned by the heat of 4,000 degrees and lay scorched black and carbonised.

I was not able to find my brother and sister, although there were a heap of dead bodies around the district. All that I could see were burned bricks, roof tiles, and dead bodies.

I did not have any relatives in Nagasaki, because my father had been transferred there as a stationmaster. So from that day, having no place to sleep except an area swept by the flames, I slept with my parent's dead bodies at night. During the daytime, I tried to find my brother and sister in vain. As I had nothing to eat, I had to drink water from the river, where a lot of dead bodies were floating.

On August 15, the war was over as a consequence of Japan's unconditional surrender. By that day, my body had changed. I had black bleeding from the gums, and I was not able to walk because of fierce shivers caused by high fever. Under that condition, I left Nagasaki, on August 17, having my parent's bones in front of my chest, and I entered hospital in our home town.

On September 19, the headquarters of General Mac Arthur set up a press code, ordering us never to speak about the atomic bombs. They carried the materials relating to the atomic effects back to the United States. They staunchly announced that all the persons who should die of radiation effect, would die by December 1945. Those who would live at that time, would have been spared by the radiation. Therefore, the actual situation of the radiation injuries was not known to the people, even in Japan. For example, a doctor who examined me, treated me as if I had syphilis or gonorrhea, because I was prone to be tired, to bleed, and I suffered from purpura and diarrhea.

In 1957, the Supporting Law of Atomic Victims was passed, and I was legally admitted as a Hibakusha. But I was not able to feel relieved, because if people knew that I was a Hibakusha, I would not be able to get a job nor to get married. People would hate me, because of my incapacity of working hard, caused by radiation. I had to conceal my being a Hibakusha, in order to survive.

In 1963, I suddenly got a high fever, 18 years after my exposition to radiation. My body changed stiff and black. I became just like one of the dead bodies I had seen at the ruins of fires in the city of Nagasaki. It took me three years to get back my original skin colour. During those years, I was extremely scared during the night, at times hearing the voices of the dead.

Through this experience, I awakened to the cruelty and the danger of radiation and I became involved in the anti-nuclear movement. I narrated the actual situation of Hibakushas at both "Global Conferences of Atomic Victims" in New York and in Berlin.

As I have no parents nor children, I can work actively in the movement and openly introduce myself as a Hibakusha. If I had any children, I would surely conceal my being a Hibakusha, because the second and the third generations of Hibakushas are now confronted with the difficulty of getting married.

As you know, on January 17, 1995, the Hanshin Earthquake occurred in Japan and caused tremendous damage. My city Osaka, which is located about 25 kilometres from Kobe, also shook violently. When I watched on TV the city of Kobe burning, blowing up black smoke, and the houses overthrown, the cruel scenes of the atomic raid 50 years before suddenly revived, and consequently, I had a high temperature, hearing the dead people crying during the night, and it became impossible for me even to stand up.

Through this experience, I realised that the radiation of the atomic bomb has not yet gone out of my body, after so many years. Although ABCC began to investigate the damage of the droppings of atomic bombs, and they inspected Hibakushas, they only gathered Hibakushas together to examine them, offering no suitable way of treatment. So a friend of mine who moved from Hiroshima to Osaka, stopped returning to Hiroshima because of ageing and fatigue, although she had gone back to Hiroshima for a long time, complying with the request of ABCC.

We, who underwent the war, have endured the disasters and illnesses caused by the atomic bombings, and we repent on our having caused the war, and think that our sufferings were the punishment of heaven brought on us.

But we never wanted commercial nuclear power, which surely destroys human bodies and nature. To possess nuclear power, I believe, represents a violation of the international law. I sincerely ask you to work to lower the standard dose of radiation exposure, and to make a new world possible, in which we, Hibakushas, will be able to live without anxiety, as well as all the people in the world.

Thank you very much for your kind attention.

The President :

Thank you very much, Ms. Yamashina.

Dr. Gadekar wants the floor to add some precision on the method she used in Rajasthan.

You have the floor.

Dr. Sanghamitra Gadekar :

Thank you very much.

Why did we do our survey in Rajasthan ? We wanted to find out whether the people living in the vicinity of nuclear power plants were taking any benefit from them, and secondly, to find out the price they had to pay in terms of health. We went from door to door, house to house. The data regarding demography, economic, educational and health status were collected. A team of doctors clinically examined each and every person. No laboratory tests or X ray examinations were performed. We found many similarities in the distant villages and the proximate villages, but there were also some great differences.

The similarities were in short duration diseases : fevers, acute infections like urinary tract infections, heart disease and vascular disease. These diseases were similar in both areas.

The differences were especially in the reproductive system, menstrual disorders, lack of libido and childless couples, (people who had not conceived at all, or couples who had conceived but had never given birth to a live child). Other differences were the chronic eye problems and the tumours. Solid tumours were seven times as high in the proximate villages, compared to the distant villages. The eye problems were 5 times as high. The digestive problems and skin diseases were also quite high in the proximate villages compared to the distant villages. As to the "Bura-Bura" disease, that is observed in the Hiroshima and Nagasaki survivors, we see a similar pattern around the Indian reactors, where there are extremely low doses, according to the government.

Our findings confirm those of our Russian colleagues who have studied low-dose radiation effects. We see that people in India, exposed to low doses over a long time, are suffering from the same kinds of diseases.

As mentioned yesterday, the negative pregnancy outcomes are significantly greater near the nuclear power plant. Also the number of people complaining of sterility is greater. The numbers of abortions and stillbirths are far larger, the numbers of babies who die within a few hours of birth are much larger. More genetically deformed babies are born. These huge differences cannot be explained away by unsanitary living conditions, neither by differences in the ages of childbearing mothers. These are the things of which we were accused by the Indian officials.

At the beginning, the government told us that these findings were due to the educational status : poor people are not hygienic, they have very bad living conditions, the mothers are very old. They told us this without having done any survey on maternity ages or anything. They just pulled these reasons out of their hats. We checked out all family variables : in the proximate villages and the distant villages, the family size was almost the same, the number of families with women as the head of the household was also similar, average pregnancy age were the same and the women's age at marriage was very similar, in both the proximate and the distant villages.

We have established a very strong data-base for our results, and they stood up in front of the whole of the establishment. They had always been saying this and that, without any facts. When they were confronted with our facts, they could not say anything.

Looking at the diseases rate in both places, we see that there was a premature-ageing process : in the proximate villages, diseases of the old age affected ten years younger patients than in the distant villages. We confirmed a pattern observed before by Dr. Bertell and by other researchers, that is a premature ageing of people living in the vicinity of the Rajasthan nuclear plant. Radiation increase the ageing process, by causing a gradual accumulation of mistakes in the body's homeostatic mechanisms, and that is the process that we see.

I would request the Judges to look upon the evidences available in the literature, and not to consider the Chernobyl accident as an isolated accident. It is a very sad catastrophe. Enough experimentation with radiation on people has been done.

We in the scientific community know, everyone knows, that radiation are harmful, and that they produce this kind of damages. Now this has gone on for a long time, and we have enough evidence of its effects on human beings. First it was proven in the laboratory in cell tests etc., but now everyone can see the effects on living persons. If we don't do anything now, it will be too late.

The President :

I thank you, Dr. Gadekar.

I now give the floor to Dr. Sadamori.

Dr. Kazue Sadamori :

I am a pharmacist working in a hospital located south of Osaka. First, I would like to talk about my fundamental views on radiation injuries.

The experiences of Hiroshima, Nagasaki and Chernobyl teach us that radiation injury is neither a local nor a national problem. It is a global problem we have to solve, in order to ensure the existence of all sorts of life on our planet. I think that one should grasp the radiation injuries of Hiroshima, Nagasaki and Chernobyl, as one of the problems related to the protection of our global environment.

I will talk about the work of my hospital. The fact-finding surveys of the atomic bomb survivors, which were mentioned in her talk by Dr. Furitsu, are the results of the efforts of our hospital's staff. I would also like to talk about my own activities against radiation exposure, and the lessons I learned from them.

1. Medical Activities of the Hannan Chuo Hospital :

Our hospital, Hannan Chuo Hospital, is a polyclinic with about 300 beds for patients. It was established in 1973, in an area where people, who have been traditionally discriminated in the Japanese society, were living. Its establishment was the result of efforts of doctors and medical staff, who were demanding a democratic medical policy, and of the efforts of the discriminated people themselves, who were demanding the abolition of their discrimination. Our hospital is now playing the role of a central hospital in the Matsubara City.

Our hospital offers medical care not only to the discriminated people, but also to atomic-bomb survivors, temporary workers exposed in nuclear power plants, and patients affected by the Minamata disease. Those people have been discriminated against, without receiving adequate medical care. The motto of the hospital is to understand the situation of these patients.

The members of the Investigative Committee of Atomic Bomb Victims of the Hannan Chuo Hospital, have been trying to improve the health of workers, who have been suffering from health disorders due to radiation exposure.

We conducted a fact-finding survey. It included surveys not only on health problems, but also on actual conditions of life, and on jobs. We tried to investigate the exposure. The survey was carried out from 1979 to 1982, with the help of members of a local trade-union and of a group of scientists. The results of this survey are valid, although the scale of the survey is small.

In 1985, 40 years after the atomic bombing, we have undertaken a study on the health disorders of atomic-bomb survivors, and their effects on their lives and jobs. We continued this investigation until 1995. For the 50th anniversary of the atomic bombings, in solidarity with the demands of the movement of the Hiroshima/Nagasaki survivors, we demanded the immediate enactment of the National Compensation Law of Hibakusha (A-Bomb Victim survivors).

For the 10th anniversary of Chernobyl, our organisation proposed to undertake a study of the victims of the catastrophe. After discussing our ideas with activists, physicians, teachers and people living in the contaminated areas, we prepared a research protocol, which is now used in Belarus and will soon be used in Ukraine. We want to confront the IAEA with the real consequences of the radiation.

We share the concerns of the victim's movements, and work with them to collect dates on the health consequences. Together with them, we shout : "Never again Chernobyl". It is absolutely necessary that general diseases, different from thyroid cancers, be considered as being consequences of Chernobyl. In particular, the "Genbaku Bura-Bura" disease must be recognised as a consequence of radiation exposure.

I would like to call on you, Judges of this Tribunal, to consider the following points in your Verdict :

The United Nations and the World Health Organisation have publicly recognised the thyroid cancers as caused by the effects of radiation exposure, due to the Chernobyl accident. However they refuse to recognise other cancers. This is an underestimation of Chernobyl, according to the duration of the radiation exposure, and the kind of radioactivity. However, we should learn from the experience of Hiroshima and Nagasaki. Cancers among atomic bomb survivors have been increasing, even now, 50 years after the bombings. As the result of the reassessment of the atomic-bomb radiation dosimetry (DS86), the ICRP itself has conceded that their former risk-estimates of radiation-induced leukemia and cancers, were underestimated by at least 5 times. Recent studies show that the cancer risk-estimates of atomic-bomb survivors, based on the incidence data, are greater than those based on the mortality dates. According to these studies, the risk of cancer during 50 years after the bombings can at least be estimated about 15 times higher as that estimated by the ICRP.

After the Chernobyl accident, the ICRP recommended the radiation dose level for relocation to be 1 Svt (ICRP Publication 63, 1992). This was an easing of the former level : 500 mSvt in the first year, as recommended in 1984 (ICRP Publication 40). Exposed to a level of 1 Svt, people would surely suffer acute radiation symptoms after a short period. We can never accept such a recommendation. It means actually that the people do not have to be evacuated from most of the contaminated areas. Instead of setting such radiation level for relocation, they should stop the nuclear power plants, the origin of all nuclear accidents and radiation exposures. We therefore demand that they abolish all the nuclear power plants and convert over their energy policy towards a safer and sustainable one.

The "Genbaku Bura Bura" disease is a common radiation injury, that can be seen not only among atomic bomb victims, but also among exposed workers in nuclear power plants, down-winders of Hanford, of nuclear facilities, uranium miners of American indigenous people and Chernobyl victims. This fact shows that many symptoms of Chernobyl victims should be treated as radiation injuries, caused by the Chernobyl accident. We cannot regard them as diseases only caused by psychological effects or anxiety. The governments of Ukraine, Belarus and Russia should compensate them for these symptoms.

According to the reassessment of the atomic bomb radiation dosimetry, and the recent results of risk estimates based on the cancer incidence in atomic bomb survivors, the ICRP should cut sharply the radiation exposure limits for the general public and the nuclear workers, to levels at least of 10th lower than that of their recommendation.

According to the released abstracts of the background papers, as a basis for the discussion at the IAEA Conference's topical sessions, the IAEA do not concede any cancers other than thyroid cancer, no neonatal disorders nor many symptoms like "Bura Bura Disease", as caused by the radiation after the Chernobyl accident. They do not discuss future effects, saying that "nothing is certain" for the time being. They also underestimate the radiation doses, the cancer risk and the number of victims (800,000 liquidators, 3.7 million residents in contaminated areas).

Moreover, even for thyroid cancers, that is the only disease they contend as radiation effects, they stress that they are not fatal, saying "thyroid cancers, if properly treated, do not carry a high mortality."

They also stress the need for studies, to observe and predict future effects or increases of concern. However, they intend to study them, not for protecting the health, nor for giving relief to the victims, but for promoting their nuclear policy, providing for even more victims in cases of future severe accidents. They are treating the Chernobyl victims as "guinea pigs", in order to carry on their pro-nuclear policy. We can never accept it !

Thank you very much, Dr. Sadamori. Thank you for all your documents.

Now we shall listen to the experts. I give the floor to Dr. Bertell.

Dr. Rosalie Bertell :

Our President did ask this morning a question about the releases of radioactivity from nuclear plants during routine operations, and he asked if there was any way to stop it. We have to realise that the radionuclides are atoms, radioactive atoms, formed in a nuclear reaction. They occur in different states, some are liquids, some are solids and some are gases.

Routinely, all of the gases are released and all of the liquids are released, so the only effort made is to retain the solid radionuclides. When we talk about radioactive waste, it's that solid portion only. By the design of the technology, we don't know any way to constantly collect and store a gas. We just keep getting more and more gases, because we can't contain them physically.

So what happens with the industry, is that they try to set a standard, and they say that as long as you keep the releases of gases and liquids below this standard, we'll consider it acceptable to the population. If you go above that, it's unacceptable. When you do that, and give those numbers to the engineers, they design an industry in order to be legal - everybody assumes that if it's legal, it's safe.

I would just like to compare for you the regulation settings in the nuclear industry and in the chemical industry, using cancer as the endpoint, since both the chemical and the nuclear industry are well known to induce cancers. We can't compare everything, but we should be able to compare cancers.

If I only take one of these radionuclides, and we are talking of 300-500 different ones, but I'll just take Tritium. This is a radioactive isotope of Hydrogen. Tritium is usually released as tritiated water, which is radioactive water. It comes out as steam, or it is dumped into the local river or lake. The standards that were originally set in 1952, by the nuclear physicists who worked on the atomic bomb, were applied between 1952 and 1990 as the international recommended levels. According to that standard, in Ontario, we were allowed 40,000 Bq/litre of drinking water. This was considered the standard, and then they tried to operate below that.

In 1990, after a lot of international pressure, and after the reassessment of the atomic bomb data, they lowered the permissible dose to the public. In response to that, the nuclear industry said that they would reduce those 40,000 down to 7,000 Bq/litre. This standard was asked to be reviewed by our ACES (Advisory Committee on Environmental Standards), which deals with all pollutants. All chemical pollutants go to this Committee, so they used the same standard approach when it came to Tritium. They used the industry estimates of how much they release and what the risk of cancer are, and they called for an immediate, emergency reduction to 100 Bq/l and within 5 years to get it down to 20 Bq/litre.

There is a big difference between 40,000 and 20 Bq/l. If you deal with engineers and physicists, they look at the standard and say, we stayed below it, and therefore we are safe. If you talk to medical people, they'll say that the standards are not protecting health. Therefore, to be in compliance with standards, does not always protect the worker, nor the public health.

This, I think, is the basis of the dispute. People are talking two different languages, and if we could do something to bridge this dispute, between what is legal and what is safe, I think we would be doing quite a service.

The workers and the public are often deceived by standards, they expect that a standard is there to protect them. Therefore, if they're told their radiation exposure is within permissible limits, they think that they shouldn't be sick, or that it's their imagination or that nothing is connected. I think it is a big part of the problem.

The President :

I thank Dr. Bertell for those very useful explanations. Are there any questions from the Judges ?

Judge Corinne Kumar :

I want to express a word of special thanks to Ms. Yamashina, our speaker from Japan. I think you are a miracle in how you have survived. The pain that you offer us is a strength that you offer us. I want to thank you.

Hiroshima and Nagasaki became a huge laboratory for nuclear scientists after the bombings, when the rational science took over. These studies were often not used to help the Hibakusha, but to promote nuclear power stations.

The Hibakusha themselves have led a very long struggle to get a compensation, which is still very insufficient. And I think that the term of compensation is a quite inappropriate one, when talking of sufferings that last for the whole life. I think it is very important for us to understand the struggle of the victims of the atomic bombings, and to compare it to the fate of the victims of Chernobyl : an official denial of their sufferings, in order to escape to compensate them, and to acknowledge the real threats posed by the commercial nuclear industry.

Judge Mitsuo Okamoto :

I have a question to Dr Katsumi Furitsu. In observing Hiroshima and Nagasaki diseases and Chernobyl diseases, there is a difference between Hiroshima and Nagasaki, where the radiation came primarily from outside, whereas in Chernobyl, they incorporated radiation internally. Do you still think that the "Bura-Bura" disease and diseases observed in Chernobyl have something very much in common ?

The President :

I give the floor to Dr. Furitsu.

Dr. Katsumi Furitsu :

Even though the irradiation are somewhat different in some points, I think there are many common aspects of the diseases. In Hiroshima and Nagasaki, there were also to some degree amounts of internal irradiation. And in Chernobyl, in the contaminated areas, there is an external and an internal irradiation, so we must consider both internal and external irradiation in both cases.

The biggest difference between the irradiation of Hiroshima and Nagasaki and Chernobyl, is that in the contaminated area, people have been exposed to the irradiation for many years, and maybe will be in the future, whereas in Nagasaki and Hiroshima, a relatively short period was experienced.

Judge Okamoto :

Can you explain to us the problem of the compensations ?

Dr. Katsumi Furitsu :

As you know, Hibakusha have been demanding a national compensation law. After the war, Japan demanded compensations from the United States who dropped the atomic bombs on Nagasaki and Hiroshima.

We have been demanding a direct compensation from the Japanese government to the movement of Hibakusha. Even as Hibakusha have been struggling for over 40 or 50 years, the Japanese government has not yet given the actual minimum for national compensation.

Dr. Kazue Sadamori :

Some kind of allowance is given to Hibakusha. When they suffer from certain kinds of diseases, they have to fill certain documents, and after that they can get at most about one thousand dollars per month for special diseases like cancers and leukemia. Only the Hibakusha who were very close to ground zero can apply. It is very hard to get such compensations, and most of the Hibakusha get another kind of compensation, that is about 30,000 yen a month, which is 300 dollars.

Dr. Sanghamitra Gadekar :

The question of compensation in Rajasthan is quite different from the case of Hiroshima or Chernobyl. The government has been very keen to find out the names of the victims, their photographs, etc., without doing any work, without going and visiting the villages. They are trying to find this out from me, so that they can give people some money and buy them off, which creates problems in the vicinity, with some people being given some money, and some people not. For these people, or any people living in the vicinity of nuclear power plants, or where there is radiation fallout,

170

the effects which do not show up now, will show up in the future, again and again. It will go from bad to worse.

Therefore, the question of compensation is a question which should be thought of very seriously. I don't mean to say that victims who are suffering should not be treated. I don't say they should not be given any money to support them, but the question is very complicated, and needs to be considered thoroughly, before we go into compensatory action.

I feel that the whole of humanity, all the future generations are at risk when it comes to nuclear power. Who is going to compensate, and how is one going to compensate ? The only important question one has to think about is how can we stop it now, in order not to produce any more radionuclides which were not there before. We must not increase the radioactive levels and doses, especially radionuclides like Plutonium, which is man made. The way to compensate is by stopping nuclear power, and not by giving money, that can be done, but that is not a global solution to the problem.

<u>The President :</u>

I thank you, Dr. Gadekar.

We now come to our last session.

7. RESPONSES OF NATIONAL AND INTERNATIONAL AGENCIES

Speakers :　　Dr. Vladimir Iakimets, Institute for Systems Analysis, Russian Academy of Sciences, Board of the Nevada-Semipalatinsk Movement, Moscow

Dr. Katsumi Furitsu, Investigative Committee of Atomic Bombing Victims at Hannan Chuo Hospital, Osaka, Japan

Professor Michel Fernex, University of Basle, Switzerland, International Medical Commission for Chernobyl

The President :

I give the floor to Dr. Iakimets.

Dr. Vladimir Iakimets :

I would like to thank the organisers of this Tribunal, because for me this has just been a great opportunity to listen to people from all over the world on this very important topic.

I want to start from the IAEA Conference. First of all, thanks to our Norwegian friends, I have had a chance to look through the abstracts, through the IAEA Conference papers. I would like to tell you that I found a great discovery, just published in the Abstracts volume.

I would like to quote an article written by Dr. Peter Fong of the University of Atlanta, Georgia. While I looked through this article, I found I was wrong. Professor Gould was wrong when he contributed his paper to this Tribunal, all the colleagues from Belarus, you were wrong, just wrong, and me too.

Let me read this discovery : "Recent studies show that low levels of radiation may reduce cancers", reduce ! This is the discovery !

We can read that the cancer-mortality rate in the 8 Mountain States, related to the entire United States average rate, is constantly O.752 over the past 40 years.

As natural background radiation in mountain areas are twice as compared with other areas in the United States, "we conclude that a doubling of the background radiation reduce the cancer mortality rate by 25%". Great !

What you should know, Professor Gould, is that instead of causing 120,000 cancer deaths in 30 years, it would save 3,000,000 lives and therefore nuclear energy is safe. Let me ask you, what are we doing here ? What are we talking about ? What is our problem ?

It seems to me that a very important lesson to take from this, is that there are 2 streams of thought, absolutely separated. We need to organise a real and actual dialogue between us and them. Otherwise we will listen to such kind of "discoveries", and they will increase the permissible radiation levels world-wide.

Let me now come to the main points I would like to share with you : which is a 2 years study of the activities of 3 different kinds of organisations dealing with radiation protection.

Studies were recently undertaken by the Russian Scientific Commission on Radiation Protection. I had the chance to participate in their last session, which was held on 9th February, 1996, where they discussed a new concept and the methods to introduce this new concept for territories contaminated after the Chernobyl disaster.

I will also recall the results of the Committee for Ecological Security, which is working within the National Security Council, chaired by a very respectable person from my point of view, Professor Yablokov.

I would like to finally to touch upon some activities of Non-Governmental Organisations.

For the last 3 years, there have been a lot of sessions about what kinds of changes should be introduced into the activities on state level, in order to help more optimally and rehabilitate human health and the environment. They came up with quite good results, including a register of the people who are living on these territories. They are completing a data-bank, the result of which we have seen in Professor Burlakova's presentation.

I want to give you an outline of the principle for the new concept, introduced by the Russian Scientific Commission on

Radiological Protection (RCRP), and share with you my opinion on this concept. You can also find in one of the chapters in the IAEA proceedings the new definition they give of a contaminated territory.

From now on, a contaminated territory, contains only inhabited villages and towns, excluding the forests and the lakes. They introduce an average acceptable dose, induced by accidents, higher than 0,1 Svt/year. Based on this, they have introduced two types of zones, one is the zone for radiation control, with the doses in this range, the other (1 Svt) is from now on the restricted area.

They want to use this approach to permit the transition between yesterday and tomorrow. If they do so, because of the lack of previous data, there will remain a high range of uncertainty for citizens who will live in the contaminated areas, not knowing the real data for the doses they absorb.

In order to make the transition from the current approach to zoning, which is mainly based on the contamination by Cesium 137, Strontium 90 and Plutonium, to the future situation, they also envisage to undertake some other measures.

By those measures I took from the draft which was distributed during the session of the RCRP, they will suppress, for large parts of the population, the privileges and compensations they get for living in contaminated areas, according to a law on social protection. The Federal Act for the Protection against Radiation, based on the new philosophy, will reduce the 57.000 square kilometres of contaminated territory to a very small territory, where the dose to the public is at least 1 Svt/year.

What are the ideas hidden behind these projects ? I have here an article by Dr. Imanaka, from Japan, where he describes the development of the dosimetry in this country. The Japanese scientists developed their first system in 1957. After 6 to 8 years, they published a new version. They analysed the dates and informations and came up with a new system in 1986. It took them therefore 30 years to create the actual system.

The Russians on the other hand, succeeded in revising their system in only 5 years. One can doubt whether this system will be scientifically sound. This is my question, but the Committee seems happy with this.

An article published by the Minister for Major Catastrophes shows what has been spent on the three chapters of the "Unified Program for the Rehabilitation of Human Health and the Environment" after the Chernobyl catastrophe. Those three chapters are following : actual measures, investments and social protection. The social protection received almost nothing and will receive even less. The organisations who work concretely for the rehabilitation will get no money.

At the same time, the Committee for Ecological Security, a very serious organisation, has published last month following datas : On a territory of 75,000 square kilometres, with a population of 40,000 inhabitants, the economic activities are very limited. There is a high morbidity and the production of non-contaminated food is impossible. This last point is the worst. The consequence is that even if the external irradiation tends to decrease slowly, the internal dose continues to increase steadily, as our colleagues from Belarus showed us.

What measures can be taken with this contaminated foods. First of all, of course a strict quality control, then put chalk in the soil and use Potassium fertilisers, which reduce the Cesium 137 absorption.

Those measures have been undertaken in three villages in a very contaminated area from the Bryansk region. They had to be temporarily suspended, because of the lack of funds. In those three villages, the cumulated internal dose has been increasing dramatically, which will have very negative consequences on the health of the population.

As a conclusion, the Chernobyl catastrophe has been a terrible disaster. At the same time, should we learn its lessons, we could use this information on the risks of the exposure of enormous numbers of people to radiation, to lead our world towards a more secure and a cleaner world and acceptable energy policies. But the data and the research have to be correct and should not violate the most elementary rules of ethic and morality.

I thank you.

The President :

I thank you, Dr. Iakimets.

I now call on Dr. Furitsu.

Dr. Katsumi Furitsu :

I want to present to the Tribunal my opinion on the past and present policy of the IAEA, regarding the Chernobyl catastrophe.

The IAEA is denying and concealing the radiation injuries around Chernobyl, to enforce their policy to develop nuclear power plants.

Though the Chernobyl accident actually caused severe radiation injuries, the governments of the United States, European countries and Japan intend to deny and conceal the facts, in order to enforce their nuclear power policies, using international organisations like the IAEA. They act aggressively, under the cover of "the international co-operation of economic powers."

This is why we cannot accept the 1991 report from the International Advisory Committee of the IAEA : "The International Chernobyl Project. Assessment of Health and Environmental Effects and Evaluation of Protective Measures," presented in Vienna, in May 1991. We cannot allow them to do such things.

In particular, we feel extremely angry that Dr. Shigematsu, chief of the Radiation Effects Research Foundation (RERF) in Hiroshima, Japan, got the post of chairman of this Committee of the IAEA. He was the one who played a very important role in drafting the report intended to relax the radiation dose limit for relocation, and also the restriction levels for contaminated food.

IAEA even assessed that the protective measures, taken by the USSR, were based on an "overestimation" of the radiation effects. The conclusion was intended to provide "scientific foundation" under the name of the "international authority", to deny the necessity of more protective measures, such as relocation from the contaminated areas where the level of Cs137 in the soil are 15 to 40 Ci/Km2. The report's recommendations are nothing but a criminal act.

As to the relocation of the people from the contaminated areas, the report actually demanded to apply the recommendation level of the ICRP, which says that it is not necessary for the public to relocate, if the individual dose level does not exceed 500 mSvt during the first year after an accident. (Pub. 40, 1984). This is also included in the recommendation of the ICRP, 1990[6] . The exposure to 500 mSvt is about equal to that received at a distance 1.7 Km from the hypocenter in Hiroshima. Exposed to such a dose level in a short period, most people would suffer acute radiation symptoms. And 1 out of 10 victims will die from cancer induced by radiation. In November 1992[7], the ICRP increased the dose for evacuation of the population to 1 Svt, which corresponds to the dose received at 1.3 km from the hypocenter in Hiroshima.

Such a dose limit as recommended by the ICRP, can never be considered as a true "protective measure" for public health and safety. It means carrying on nuclear power policies, even if this means letting people die in a major accident. They estimated the "price" of people's lives in their own way, and decided the criteria for the intervention as far as getting the maximum economical benefits, even if this creates victims.

The cost-benefit theory, or the principle of "As Low As Reasonable Achievable : ALARA" translates differently in different countries, according to their economic situation. Therefore their recommendations for developing countries would be three times higher than in developed countries. They intend to develop nuclear technology in the developing countries, which would create more radiation victims there.

In their 1992 report, the ICRP recommended the limit to occupational dose in emergencies to O.5 Svt/year. This means that they still want to promote nuclear power, even after the accident of Chernobyl. We cannot accept such recommendations and must make them to change their recommendations.

As far as the IAEA and the WHO are concerned, they support this philosophy. I couldn't attend the IAEA Conference this week. But from what I read in the background papers, I can see that they try to find reasons in order to justify the continuation of their nuclear policy.

---

6. ICRP : "Protection of the Public in the Event of Major Radiation Accidents : Principles and Planning". ICRP Publication 40. Annuals of the ICRP, 14, No 2, 1984.

7. ICRP : "Principle for Intervention for Protection of the Public in a Radiological Emergency", ICRP, Publication 63, 1992.

In the conclusions, they insisted first of all on their high security culture which they want to increase. This talking of "safety culture" is a nonsense I think.

As to the consequences of the radiation injuries, they only mentioned the thyroid cancers, even denying leukemia. The main concern is that they deny the injuries in order to take initiatives to "improve nuclear safety" in their own way.

They also recommended to the ICRP to develop concepts for radiation protection in the case of accidents, which are "geared towards practical implementation". I do not understand exactly what they mean by this, but it can very well mean increasing the exposure limits for relocation, evacuation etc.

I think that the IAEA is now playing a more and more important role to promote the nuclear policy, for instance by influencing other international organisations like the United Nations, the World Health Organisation, using the conference of the WHO, the conference of the EU in Minsk, this Conference here in Vienna, and in a few days, the G 7 Summit in Moscow on "Nuclear Safety".

I want to propose here that the participants to this Tribunal should send a protesting note to the G 7, demanding that everything should be undertaken to take back the permission to people to return where they have been evacuated before, in contaminated areas with more than 15 Curie/km2. This is a very dangerous policy.

The President :

Thank you, Dr. Furitsu.

I now give the floor to Professor Fernex.

Professor Michel Fernex :

Mr. President, dear Judges, dear Friends,

I bring to this Tribunal the report I have been writing on the WHO Conference held in Geneva, in November 1995. I was also in Minsk during the Conference organised by the Department of Energy (DoE) of the United States and the European Commission. I was impressed by the first page of the program, the title of this Conference : "Future Accidents", not in the singular, but plural.

Administrations seem to consider that it is essential to prepare for the coming accidents. They are well aware, and it has been said at the IAEA congress in Vienna, that it is the same as for the war : you always prepare for the wrong war, and you are always surprised. I think that they were correct in this assumption.

In Minsk, I participated in the Conference organised by the "Foundation for the Children of Chernobyl", March 21 and 22, 1996. It was an important meeting. Dr. Grushevaya, who was one of the organiser, has already presented the report of this Conference to the Tribunal.

Increased neonatal malformations were seen among children born in irradiated regions, with a statistically significant increase for four different deformities, when comparing 1982 to 87, with 1988 to 1992. For some malformations, there were more deformities in populations living in areas contaminated with only 1 - 5 Curie/km2. This confirms the findings of Professor Burlakova as to the high effects of relatively lower doses of radiation. Resettlement of people in such areas was discussed. It is criminal for the children who will born there.

We heard also about a significant increase of cancers in liquidators working for more than 30 days in the contaminated surrounding of Chernobyl. Similar increases of malignancies are starting to appear among people evacuated from contaminated areas as well as in the general population. In Belarus, there will soon exist no more control population, i.e. people which are not contaminated, for the reasons indicated by Prof. Nesterenko : food is contaminated, especially with Strontium 90.

This conference published several resolutions, addressed to the Judges here, which we should support. They stress the immense sufferings of hundreds of thousands of people. They insist on the fact that Chernobyl is not behind us, but in front of us. For the majority of the victims, the cancers as a consequence of the Chernobyl accident are not yet clinically evident, their number is increasing now, and will continue to increase for the next 20 to 40 years.

Among the recommendations of the Conference, one was the necessity to look for alternative, renewable sources of energy, for energy savings, and to close down the nuclear facilities.

The participants also asked for international help for the country to recover. This message is intended to all of us, we must act. The damage will persist, and part of the country is lost for generations. The genetic damages in human, children, animals, plants may not find their end before many generations have passed.

In official conferences, we hear about research going on around Chernobyl, conducted by scientists from several countries. Very often, the same subjects were chosen or imposed. E.g., hundreds of millions dollars are spent for studies on the only recognised malignant tumour : the thyroid cancer in children. Nothing or very little is spent on other diseases, such as diabetes mellitus or teratology. Money is missing for medicaments and laboratory tests for the treatment of all diseases, including thyroid cancers after puberty.

We heard Dr. Mirnyi speaking of the liquidators. He was not a volunteer. He was sent there to perform a job. He and the other liquidators working with him were exposed to radiation close to the exploded Chernobyl reactor. They had to stay there for a month. They were obliged to receive the maximal dose accepted for workers in accidental situations, and this every day. Blood was taken from the veins from all the liquidators, many times, without any explanation.

Since Nuremberg, human trials conducted by physicians, including withdrawing blood for any study, have to be medically or scientifically justified. This always requires "informed consent". For liquidators, there was no information whatsoever. This has to be considered as a professional misbehaviour, as it happened long after Nuremberg and after Helsinki. It was also criminal to expose people in that manner, especially as they were often just waiting outside to reach their full daily dose.

I was at the IAEA meeting this week. This was not a scientific meeting, apparently just a propaganda meeting in support of the nuclear industry. To be invited there, we had to apply to the Ministry of Foreign Affairs, to the Ministry of Industry, with copies to the Society for Nuclear Energy. The Ministry responsible for Public Health was not consulted. After this, my wife and I (as past-President of IPPNW-Switzerland) became members of the official Swiss Delegation.

The IAEA recognised three diseases. The first is the acute

irradiation syndrome. Among several hundred cases, some died. Experts discussed about numbers : 31 or 32 deaths. In fact the others survived and if they died in the following years, the cause of death was labelled as "natural". For instance 8 or 9 died from myocardial infarction, which was said to be absolutely "natural" in 40 year old healthy men. Four died of rare infections, or tuberculosis. I stood up and said : "I am an infectiologist. These infections among young men correspond to what we would expect in AIDS."

Diabetes mellitus was also mentioned as a cause of death, and was said to be not related to the irradiation. However, the Minister of Health in Ukraine stated at the WHO Conference in November 1995, that there is a 25% increase of diabetes mellitus in his country since the accident. The same increase is found in Belarus and Russia. In Gomel, the cases of insulin-dependent diabetes mellitus doubled among children, as compared with 5 years earlier.

There is in fact a new disease occurring in these areas : a malignant form of diabetes, in very young children. Children are hospitalised in coma : it is very difficult to bring them back to life with insulin. These are cases of insulin-dependant, very unstable diabetes, which provoke now a kind of epidemic in these areas. I asked : "What is your opinion on this ?"

My question about diabetes was answered in the following way. The IAEA chairperson said : "We have in this hall the best specialists on radiation-induced diseases. Has anyone seen any link between diabetes and radiation ?" As there was no immediate reaction from the audience, he said : "All specialists of the world are here, none raised the hand. You see, there exists no such relation."[8] This is the way discussions were conducted at the IAEA Conference.

Hashimoto thyroiditis also occurred in a young population after the accident, a disease described in Japan after the A bomb. It is an auto-immune disease. Insulin-dependent diabetes mellitus and Hashimo's disease are both auto-immune diseases : the antibodies which should protect the subjects destroy their thyroid gland, or the insulin-producing cells. Professor Titov, Professor Pelevina and others have shown that the immune system is affected in all irradiated children.

---

8. This part of the discussion has been deleted in the IAEA Conference Proceedings (Sept. 96)

Besides auto-immune diseases, new infections appear, or more severe infectious diseases : viral cold degenerates in sinusitis, which leads to brain abscesses in children. Such complications were extremely rare earlier. Bronchitis leads to pneumonia, and to necrotic pneumonia, also in small children, when the immune system is damaged.

At the IAEA Conference, I understood that science may be used to <u>not demonstrate</u> any relation between a disease and an accident. This negative research requires a special technique, which has been explained by Professor Viel. The methodology which is being used when experts want to have inconclusive results, first requires to select wrong indicators : for instance, if looking for cancers, you will have to choose mortality instead of morbidity, as to die of cancers requires time; the study must be published before death occurs. You can also look for the wrong pathology, looking for stress or liver cirrhosis instead of diabetes mellitus.

It is also necessary to choose the wrong timing, as shown above, the study must end during the latent phase for solid tumours. It makes it easy to state in the conclusions of such a trial, that there are no radiation-induced cancers. It is also important not to choose the most sensitive groups, women or small children.

At the end of such trials, you are able not to find any statistical differences, and then you (the expert of the IAEA on teratology) do not recognise the evidence, i.e. that it is difficult to demonstrate phenomena which may be uncommon, but conclude that there exists no relationship between the event and the studied pathology. Such experts feel satisfied and continue to promote nuclear power plants.

Viel quotes Adorno, saying : "Scepticism regarding what has not been proven may easily become prohibition to think". During the whole IAEA Conference, I had the feeling that we were not allowed to consider any other diseases than those which were officially accepted.

Cancers of the thyroid were so obvious, that they could not be hidden any longer. They had been rejected for a long time, good medical revues had refused to publish the evidence. At the IAEA, Professor Williams from Cambridge, an outstanding scientist said : "These cancers exist." This form was exceedingly rare before. These are very malignant cancers. When diagnosed, 80% of the children show metastases in the lymph nodes or in the lung, or both. "But these are good cancers" said Prof. Williams in his conclusion. The lady sitting next to me, member of the official French delegation said : "Well, I am happy that my two daughters do not have this kind of good cancer".

For mothers, families, and for the patients, this is not at all a "good" cancer. It may be cured by often devastating surgery, with the risk of withdrawing parathyroid glands. In any case, the prognosis remains unknown, as it is a new disease. It is furthermore an endocrine disease : children will have to be treated for their whole life with hormones. The first question children asked in a survey, performed in the pediatric hospital of Minsk was : "Will I be able to have children ?" (60% of the victims are girls.) Who is really able to answer?

At the IAEA Conference, arrogant attitudes were common. A speaker claimed : "The only significant difference I found between people living in contaminated areas and others, is that they drink more Vodka." He laughed after this remark. The arrogance was also present when speakers said : "Instead of killing reindeers and paying millions of dollars to the Sami in Sweden, governments should have taken into account some cancers, and done a better job with all this money", and other remarks of this quality.

When people discussed levels of radiation which should be considered as acceptable, the problem was essentially to reduce the costs of future accidents. It was proposed to avoid to evacuate and to resettle people. They also discussed if they should resettle the evacuated people in contaminated areas, and they concluded: "Yes we should, but it costs a lot."

The vice-director of the IAEA, Dr. Rosen, said that the cancers which will occur, will only represent a very small fraction of the millions of cancers which will occur anyhow. My answer to this is that the estimation of Dr. Rosen regarding the number of neoplasms may be underestimated by a factor of ten or more. However, cancers in a great number of children, should not be "diluted" in great numbers of cancers of old persons. With 80 years of age, human have their life behind them.

Dr Rosen was asked on the radio during the Vienna congress, whether when M. Blix, director general of the

IAEA, declared that one Chernobyl per year would be acceptable because of the advantages brought by the nuclear industry, he was really informed about the scale of the Chernobyl catastrophe. He responded : "Maybe he was not fully informed". Today, experts are apparently still not informed. They do not want to see the documents received by the Tribunal today.

We have addressed the question of lies. It is always difficult to say that experts are lying. When the official IAEA expert said : "There are no registers of deformities for genetic disorders, and therefore, as a conclusion, there are no birth defects from irradiation", I think that the official speaker was lying, and drawing official wrong conclusions.

Besides teratology, the reduction of births by 30 % in Belarus may be due to the socio-economic conditions. But it may also partly be due to sterility. Sterility has been encountered in men and women. It can be due to endocrine disorders or to lethal genetic deformities in the fetuses. We know from the studies on carp, that 70 % of the eggs present lethal mutation and do not hatch. 70 % of the survivors after six months present major deformities due to recessive mutations.

Thank you very much.

The President :

I want to thank you very much, Professor Fernex, for this very interesting presentation.

We now have the opportunity to ask questions.

Judge Mitsuo Okamoto :

I have a question for Dr. Iakimets. You were saying that one of the causes of the present situation is the existence of two languages, the one we speak here, before the Tribunal, and the official one, and you believe that we should establish a dialogue. Do you believe that a dialogue with the officials is useful ? or should we not organise hearings, for large numbers of persons who have no opinion, because they are uncommitted ? They can hear us, then they can hear them and form themselves their opinion. This is different from a dialogue between promoters and opponents.

Dr. Vladimir Iakimets :

Thank you very much for this question. I would like to answer it in the following way : I have been working for the last 6 years as a volunteer for the anti-nuclear movement Nevada- Semipalatinsk, which intended to stop nuclear tests all around the world, and we did it. It was the movement that succeeded in closing the Semipalatinsk test site.

In Russia, we have a lot of problems with nuclear weapons. At some time, we understood that the only way to progress was to establish a dialogue, to sit at the table with our adversaries and to discuss with them, and say what you have to say. A dialogue may be possible through public hearings, but this is more like lectures. We have to show our adversaries what they do not want to see. We can even bring them to the Chernobyl area, so that can see with their own eyes the increase of diseases.

Judge Freda Meissner-Blau:

I have a question to Professor Fernex. You said that the IAEA Conference was a propaganda battle for the nuclear industry. Could you tell us : was there no opposition ? no possibility for any opposition ? did the delegates of the concerned countries, Ukraine, Belarus and Russia accept all this ?

Judge Elmar Altvater :

I have a question in the same direction. In most United Nations Conferences, there usually is also an NGO meeting or some Forum, like in Rio, or Berlin for the Climate Conference in 1995. Was there some similar meeting of NGOs ? Was one requested, in order to attract the attention of this official body to what is called the civil society, the international civil society concerned with these questions, which are international questions ? Everybody has the right to know, and is entitled to participate in this discussion, and to participate in some way in the decision making.

Judge Surendar Gadekar :

Professor Fernex, you mentioned an increasing sterility, and possible explanations for the drop in birth rates. In Rajasthan, we also found an increased number of childless couples, and there is a growing number of negative pregnancy outcomes. Nevertheless, we see an increase in the number of children, that is because people try to compensate for the increased risks of stillbirths or neo-natal deaths. I would think that the drop in the birth-rate in Belarus, has maybe to do with an increase of the sterility, but also with the demoralisation of the people, who are no more willing to live.

Judge Corinne Kumar :

Professor Fernex, you said that the research and survey should be ethical. I want to ask you whether this kind of research is not inherent to modern science, to the kind of knowledge and knowledge systems we have encapsulated in today's science, to the conceptual distance between the object and the subject, the observed and the observer, the poverty and the poor. There is no connection between them. Therefore must we not find another way, where ethics inform the scientific discourse ?

Judge Mitsuo Okamoto :

I would like to raise a question on the links between the civil and the military atomic technology. The IAEA is the surveillance authority for all nuclear facilities and nuclear material in all countries having ratified the Non-Proliferation Treaty (NPT), which was prolonged indefinitely in May 1995. It seems that the IAEA takes this mandate very seriously, to see that nuclear technology is not used for military objectives. At the same time, civil and military nuclear technologies are very similar. What do you think ?

The President :

Thank you.

Could you please respond to those questions ?

Professor Michel Fernex :

You were asking if there was propaganda or a free discussions. The WHO, another organisation of the United Nations, organised six months earlier an open conference in Geneva. Physicians could attend and take part in the discussions. They could present papers not depending on a political selection, as in Vienna.

186

The aim of the IAEA meeting was "Summing up the consequences of the accident". The Agency wanted to conclude one decade after Chernobyl, to declare that the problems had been solved : 31 or 32 persons died of acute radiation sickness; about 600 children suffered from thyroid cancer, a disease which may be cured; liquidators would have to be followed up, as some of them were exposed to rather high doses, some cancers in excess may be expected; in utero irradiation may lead to mental retardation; finally hundreds of thousands of people suffered or still suffer from stress, mainly because they were displaced and/or misinformed. Stress must be considered as the worse consequence of the accident. Therefore, for the next accidents, authorities must with priority prevent stress. This may require avoiding to displace people from contaminated areas into less contaminated places. Before all, controlled media must exclusively transmit official information.

In fact, the IAEA did not convince, even the highly selected participants. There was no consensus in the conference hall after the first days of silence, where they tried to affirm that auto-immune diseases such as insulin-dependent diabetes mellitus could not be considered as a consequence of Chernobyl, neither other immunological diseases; that teratology had to be rejected without discussions, because the threat it represents for the nuclear industry was so obvious, and the same for genetic disorders, which could not even be discussed.

Our Tribunal has been advertised during the IAEA meeting, more than 200 invitations were distributed. Organisers apparently decided not to attend. We may consider the Tribunal as the corresponding NGO meeting.

Regarding sterility, I think that the main causes are the ones you are mentioning. There are economical and social conditions, which make families considering having children as unacceptable. Sterility is an adverse affect of radiation, as aspermia or oligospermia occur around Chernobyl.

The teratologic effects of radiation is known since the mid 30's, with Etienne Wolff's studies in Strasbourg. I remember the thalidomide trial where physicians and experts from the company explained that there were no registers, and that there was no proof that the deformities occurred because the mother had taken thalidomide tablets during their pregnancies. It couldn't be proven, because registers were not in existence.

Such a register exists in Belarus. Teratology is not restricted to Chernobyl, similar findings were shown in Rajasthan, close to atomic power plants. Ms. Hesse-Honegger has also shown that normally functioning nuclear industries are teratogenic and mutagenic. This is a major justification to stop this industry. It would be a justification for the immediate withdrawal of a drug or insecticide. Why should governments not react with similar measures as to the nuclear power plants ?

Modern research is a real problem due to its enormous cost. Dr. Slukvin has no money to continue his work on teratology in carp, bred 200 km from Chernobyl. We need other sources of money than those of the state, NGO's or foundations, independent from industry, which could pay for studies and some already do, but it is small when compared with what is required.

Regarding ethics, the IAEA appears to be neither scientific nor ethical. They are not even in charge of safety for atomic power plants. In fact one would consider that they are mainly promoters of nuclear industry, marginally preventing nuclear weapon proliferation except in countries which are permitted to develop and accumulate such weapons. We know that they failed in Pakistan, India, Israel, and perhaps elsewhere.

Professor Ross Hesketh :

Thank you for letting me speak on the question of the IAEA and the question of the use of nuclear materials for military purposes. Some 14 years ago, Dr. Hans Blix said publicly that the agency has no mandate for those nations which have already proliferated. The Agency does not deal with the use of nuclear materials in the nuclear weapons states.

The Agency's safeguards are there to prevent other nations from proliferating. They are not there, I am very specific on this, to prevent the nuclear weapons states to use nuclear materials for weapons purposes. I think that is a very important distinction, which is frequently not realised in the public sphere.

Thank you.

<u>Dr. Claus Biegert :</u>

I am a journalist from Munich, and I organised the World Uranium Hearing in Salzburg in 1992. This hearing showed that a Tribunal like this one would be necessary, even without Chernobyl. Even if all nuclear power plants would be safe, we still would have people dying, because everything begins with uranium mining, and the majority of the people in the world who are the first victims, are indigenous people.

There was a mention of the necessary dialogue with the so-called other side. I am giving to the Judges a publication by the US Department of Energy. This book was given to me by Robert de Tredici, a photographer and the founder of the Atomic Photographers Guild, of photographers from Japan, Russia, Germany, Canada and the US, who are all documenting the various steps of the nuclear chain. The United States Energy Department asked one of the photographers to document the cleanup in the United States. This book, called "Closing the Circle of the Splitting of the Atom," is a visual documentation proving that there is a mess, and the need for a clean up.

It is very remarkable that this so-called other side is confessing that we need to clean up. We never would have expected our adversaries to document the mess. So this is a first step of dialogue and I have three copies for the Tribunal.

<u>Professor Helga Kromp :</u>

I attended all four frustrating days of the IAEA Conference. If you wanted to hear any opposition in this meeting, you had to listen extremely carefully.

There were a number of scientists who, as was already said, made comments, questioned the results that were presented. For non-medical people, it was however very difficult to understand the background of these questions, and there were no answers given. It was difficult to understand that there were some contradictions.

What was clear to everyone, was that there was a clear contradiction between the statements made by the politicians of Russia, Belarus and Ukraine, and the statements of the scientists of the same countries, and of course of the scientists of the West. This intrigued me, because it was not clear to me why these Eastern scientists were accepting that practically nothing had happened, and there basically was no reason for any further medical help.

I believe one of the aspects which one should not forget, is that to be a scientist who is accepted by the IAEA, or by another international agency, is something worth being. It is therefore not so easy to stand up in such a meeting, and to declare something which makes it quite clear that you will never be asked to participate in any IAEA project in the future. I think that is something to be considered.

The politicans do not have to consider that, but the scientists do, and I think that this is one of the reasons for the differences in views. Whenever these scientists were asked a direct question, they got around to avoid answering it, and generally they didn't. Generally there was just one question after the other, then the session was over. If there was a chance to answer them, very often they just spoke in circles, and didn't answer at all. There was no dialogue, it was a one-sided affair.

It was sometimes extremely cynical. We were shown pictures of Chernobyl and the surrounding areas, which were supposed to demonstrate that this is not hell, but paradise. Everything was green and lush and beautiful, and the birds were singing, and there were cows grazing, and old people coming back who looked healthy, a 60 year old grandmother and her 80 year old mother travelled 2 weeks to get there. Now they were happy and well, and that is what we were asked to remember of Chernobyl.

Thank you.

Professor Hari Sharma :

Thank you very much for inviting me to make a few comments. I would like you to know that this year is the 100th anniversary of the discovery of radioactivity by Becquerel, on 24th February 1896. Since then, radioactivity has claimed a very large number of victims. We have only heard about the A bomb ones, and the Chernobyl explosions. As a matter of fact, Becquerel loved "his" Uranium. He kept it in his pocket all the time and got some radiation burns.

Madame Curie won 2 Nobel Prizes, and she suffered from radiation burns on her hands, even skin had to be grafted.

190

At the end, she became a victim as well. We often forget about the uranium miners, in Czechoslovakia and in the whole world, where they have lung cancers. Uranium miners continued to have lung cancers, until recently when the levels were lowered. We mustn't forget about the other victims, like the dial painters in Switzerland, the radiologists who suffer radiation damage from X-ray machines.

I wanted to remind the Tribunal here, that there are all kinds of victims, not only from the accident at Chernobyl. The level of radioactivity due to A bomb tests in the 50's and early 60's, increased the level of Tritium in air and water, the levels of Carbon 14. As a matter of fact, the determination of the age of objects will be looking cockeyed in 5000 years, because of the increase of the level of Carbon 14 in the atmosphere. Carbon 14 labelling used to be very useful for us, because we used to be able to tell the age of things, ground water etc.

I want also to come back to the question raised the other day about ALARA, and how we ought to deal with these victims. We must tell them, say what type of radiation they can have exposure to. They should be given all information, just like it is done with chemicals, where we provide information. Workers have the right to know what a particular chemical does to their health. People and workers should have the same rights with respect to radiation as well. ALARA principle can only be dictated as long as people who are exposed to radiation know nothing about it. I think that should answer your question in that respect.

Lastly, I would say that there are people who are exposed to radiation which are ignored. The pilots, the crew on an aircraft flying from Europe to India, will receive a dose of 8 millirems over that distance. Every time they fly they get 1 millirem/hour. Let's say in a month they fly 100 hours, they get 100 millirems, and the background radiation is 200 millirems per year, for everyone, from cosmic rays. You are also exposed to the radiation at home, depending where it is build and how it is built. We should consider all the sources of radiation, and ask ourselves what to do with these radiation sources. We should not really get too specific about nuclear power reactors. We should consider all types of sources, if we are banning them, or whatever decision we come to, because we do have sources, which are 100 million Curie of Cobalt 60 for sterilising food etc. We should consider all aspects of radiation.

Thank you very much.

<u>Professor Jay Gould :</u>

There is a big difference between natural radiation and what happened with the nuclear age. The difference happens to be that ingested fission products such as radioactive Iodine, Strontium and all the rest, did not exist in nature prior to the nuclear age. So we have had cancer for the duration of the human experience, because of exposure to background radiation, and there should of course be standards to protect people, who fly up in the air, who are exposed to natural background radiation.

But we are talking about the nuclear age, which has introduced a completely different kind of exposure. Low-level radiation has nothing to do with background radiation. Low-level radiation refers to the internal radiation for those who are unfortunate enough to ingest fission products. That is a subject which is completely different, it marks a difference, between what knowledge we had of the dangers of radiation in the days where radiologists were exposed, and what happened in 1943, when the nuclear age began.

<u>The President :</u>

Thank you very much.

8. Conclusion :

Speakers :   *Ms. Nuala Ahern, Member of the European Parliament*

Dr. Rosalie Bertell, International Medical Commission for Chernobyl, Toronto

The President :

I will now give the floor to Ms. Nuala Ahern.

Ms. Nuala Ahern :

Thank you M. President.

I would like to introduce myself to you again. I am a member of the European Parliament from Ireland. I represent Lanster, which is the largest constituency on the East coast of Ireland. I grew up opposite, very close, the closest point in Ireland to the Sellafield Nuclear plant.

Very close to my home, we had what is now known to be the largest nuclear accident, with the exception of Chernobyl and Three Mile Island, This was an accident which happened in 1957 in Windscale, now renamed Sellafield, and it was concealed and covered up for many years. Irish physicians did very careful studies on a cohort of young women, who were exposed to the fallout from the accident, while they were pubescent teenage girls. They subsequently had a very high level of birth defects, miscarriages and Downs-syndrome children. I knew some of those women, and I've worked very much with that particular problem.

I also have the honour of coming from the same country as Ms. Adi Roche, who's photographs of the Chernobyl children are on the walls here, and who started the Chernobyl Children's Project in Ireland. We take children, from Belarus particularly, to Ireland, so we are very conscious of the effects of Chernobyl on the children, because we can see them both on our television screens and in our homes.

Also we are a small agricultural country, which doesn't have nuclear power plants, so we empathise very much with the people of Belarus, upon whom this devastation fell, and who did not have nuclear power plants themselves.

What I would like to say to you, having listened both to the

IAEA Conference and to this very important alternative Tribunal, is that everywhere where there has been radiation contamination by accident or design, we can see the responses, cancers, damages to the immune system, stillbirths, thyroid cancers in children, brain damages, mental retardation, Downs syndromes, fetal abnormalities and handicapped children. Everywhere they are denied.

Chernobyl is not different, not different in the minimisation of the effects of the disaster by those in authority. Even the clearly demonstrated, significant incidence of thyroid cancer in children, was not accepted by the authorities in the initial stage, and still today, damage to the immune and blood systems, and fetal abnormalities, and brain damage in children, are still resisted as not proven, or non significant, and not due to radiation. In fact, when reading the data from the IAEA, one would be led to believe that the major effects are psychological.

The experts talk about radiophobia, but fear is a perfectly rational response to a radiation accident. The effects of radiation are real and damaging, and as a psychologist, I regard it as malpractice, to in any way accommodate to the views of the experts, that people are somehow suffering from irrational fears. These are rational fears, rational responses to a damaging and traumatic situation.

I would like to ask the Judges to consider very carefully what to do about this organisation known as the IAEA, and how, and if it can be transformed, because it is clearly denying the reality of the people on the territories affected by this particular accident. The extent of this denial is, in my view, criminal.

We've been discussing whether or not there can be dialogue. I actually spoke out at the Conference and challenged Professor Frederick Mettler, who stood over the initial report, denying there was any radiation effects. Having done that, I got an immense response from individuals from the audience, I would say covertly. Throughout the Conference, notes were passed to me, people came up to try to talk to me, although we couldn't speak the same language. I had many contacts, even from people in the radiation business. One of them, who accepted the original data in 1991, therefore went home and told his wife that it was okay, and there were no effects, and now he feels very terrible and very guilty about that. So there is a possibility of change, but it's not a change at the official level.

I have to say that the people there, the scientists of the IAEA, did have trouble with the officials from Russia, Belarus and Ukraine, who did stand up and spoke out. The politicians did stand up to the IAEA authorities. In fact, I spoke to the Ukrainian delegation afterwards, and I asked them just what were the problems that they had with the official figures. We discussed it a little while, in a very diplomatic way, and I could eventually sense their outrage on behalf of their own people, that still the IAEA were denying that there was an outcome to the accident, that the accident had caused illness, and that IAEA were only accepting psychological effects. I could feel their outrage. Even though they are caught in an economic trap, they were still outraged at what the IAEA were doing, and they did bring that forward at the Conference, and therefore there was no consensus on the IAEA figures.

I would also ask the Judges to very clearly issue an ultimatum to the IAEA, and tell them that they are not the authority responsible for public health, and they cannot speak with authority on health questions. That is for the WHO to do, and as we know, WHO organised a Conference in November, and they adopted the reports on thyroid cancers. Had they not done so, the IAEA would still be denying thyroid cancers, even that. So we have to. support and promote at the People's Tribunal, the right and responsibility of the WHO to take the pre-eminent role in this, not the IAEA.

It was also said at the IAEA Conference by somebody, who stood up and challenged the panel, that we have to separate responsibility for radiation protection from nuclear safety, because nuclear safety is about safeguarding nuclear power plants and nuclear installations, it is not about protecting people from radiation. If you promote nuclear safeguards, and spend money as we do, and put aside money for nuclear safeguarding in the EU, then we are actually increasing the funding to the nuclear technology and nuclear industry, and they are very ready to have that funding, which is a lifeline to them at the moment. I would suggest, being a realist and a politician, that I would like to see the IAEA abolished, but I don't see that happening. What we could perhaps do, and what I would suggest you to consider carefully, is to try to turn it into an organisation that has a clearly defined role, to protect people from the effects of radiation, and this can only be done if national governments take this to the UN.

I will ask my government, and I'm sure they will do it, because they have battled for many years on nuclear issues, and my own government was one of the first to deal with the Non-Proliferation-Treaty (NPT), and take it to the UN. We can reform and transform the IAEA, from an institution promoting nuclear power and concealing the effects of radiation, to an institution that actually protects people.

I know that the people working in the UN generally believe in the peacekeeping role of the UN, there are people working here in Vienna who want the UN to be transformed in that way. Why not let them do it ? Why not show up the impossibility of, on the one hand promoting nuclear technology, and on the other hand peacekeeping, which is what we want the UN to do ?

I would like to say finally, that one of the things that outrages me most personally, is the way that women have been treated in this, and the genetic effects, this time bomb that has happened from this accident, that is going into the populations. I believe that this is a time-bomb, and we have not yet seen the full extent of the accident. I was actually forced to shout out on the final session, when we were told by a journalist that there were no birth defects, no genetic effects ! A journalist who was the former press secretary to Margaret Thatcher, what does he know about it ? Why was he up there on the platform, on the final day, telling us about he absence of birth defects ? That's outrageous and I am very angry about that, I was so angry I shouted at him. (Applause)

I would also like to tell you one of the things that Angela Merkel, German Minister of the Environment, said on the final summing up at the press conference, "We need more studies, we don't have enough, we can't make any recommendations, because we need more data." Now people in the West and in the IAEA can say plenty about Russian scientists and the former Soviet Union, but one thing we have to acknowledge is that there are no better scientists anywhere in the world.

The scientific Institutes of the former Soviet Union, on all the territory, they are the best in the world, the data is there, it does exist and the people here know that is the truth. If we don't have this data, it is because they are being prevented from giving them to us. I would like the Judges to address that also, because it is unacceptable that

Angela Merkel says that we don't have enough data. Who is she to say that, why is she lending the power and prestige of her position to the presidency of this Conference ?

I would like anyone who can, to challenge her politically on this particular issue, I will see that our German parliamentarians in the Green party do it also, and they will in the next few weeks, because we do have the data. It is outrageous to tell people after ten years, "Sorry we can do nothing, we still have to do further studies", that is a nonsense. That's why this wasn't a scientific Conference, it was a political propaganda Conference. I'm glad we've had this Tribunal. Lets make sure that people hear what we have said this weekend, and I rely on the Judges to make a good Judgement.

The President :

Thank you very much, Ms. Ahern.

I now give the floor to Dr. Bertell for the conclusion of our Permanent People's Tribunal's Session on Chernobyl.

Dr. Rosalie Bertell :

I want to give you some information on the International Medical Commission for Chernobyl (IMCC). At the time of the Tribunal in Bhopal, (at that particular Tribunal, I was one of the Judges), it became obvious to me, talking to the people in Bhopal, and seing the situation there, and the limits of what a Tribunal could do, that what the people needed was some medical input, they needed physicians. It was not just a matter of legal opinion on the catastrophe, it was to see what happened to the people, and to make some kind of recommendations to help them.

So after that, we started the first Medical Commission, which was the International Medical Commission on Bhopal (IMCB), and there were 15 Commissioners from 13 countries. We went to Bhopal for almost a month and planned an investigation, which was quite broad. We are still in the process of following that up, and trying to provide primary health-care centres in the actual areas where the victims live.

This is our second International Medical Commission, and it's an organisation that's new. We feel that it's really necessary to have outside scientific medical personnel, not directly involved with these major disasters, both to help the victims, and to find ways to prevent this from happening in the future.

There are Commissioners present here, and they helped to organise for this meeting and to communicate with our colleagues in Russia, Belarus and Ukraine. I would like them to help with some of the papers coming from the Chernobyl area, to get them out into the Western press. We all have contacts with people who know what journals to go to, or who know the form that is required, who can help with the editing of English, and all kinds of things that we could do to help.

We are interested in continuing in trying to get the communication out, but also to hold responsible medical people from our own area. I know that I'm going to go home and I will write to the Canadian Government, and say that I was embarrassed when I was in Vienna, because Dr. Peter Waight drew up the OCDE report presented at the IAEA meeting, and I thought it was outrageous. I think we have to do that. This is not the kind of representation we would like for our country.

We need to do more of this. We are trying to build a community of support. We are looking for interested people and ideas about how to do this, it's new, it's a networking thing and I would like to thank our colleagues from Russia, Belarus and Ukraine, who have come here, and also those who were our contact people, who said that these were the people to contact and to know, and to listen to.

It is on this human level of reaching out to one another, crossing boundaries, that I think that our hope in the future lies. Thank you very much for everyone who participated, and I do hope that this is not the end.

Judge Freda Meissner-Blau :

Well I am in the very privileged position to thank Dr. Bertell, who is the initiatior of this Tribunal's session on Chernobyl. (much applause)

Bibliography :

Anders, Günther, in Hingst, W. : Zeitbombe Radioaktivität, Orac Verlag, 1887.

Baker R.J., Ronald A., Van Den Busshe R.A., Wright A.J., Wiggins L.E., Hamilton M.J., Reat E.P., Smith M.H. Lomakin M.D. & Chesser R.K. : High levels of genetic change in rodents of Chernobyl, Nature, 25 April 1996, Vol. 380, pp. 707-708.

Bandahevsky Yu.I. and Lelevich V.V. : Clinical and experimental aspects of the effect of incorporated radionucleides upon the organism, Gomel, State Medical Institute, Belorussian Engineering Academy. Monography of the Ministery of Health of the Republic of Belarus, pp. 128. 1995.

Burlakova E.B.: Low intensity radiation: radiological aspect. Radiation Protection Dosimetry Vol. 62, No 1/2 pp. 13-18 1995, Nuclear Technology Publishing.

Drobyschewskaja I.M., Kryssenko N.A., Shakov I.G., Steshko W.A. & Okeanow A.E. : Gesundheitszustand der Bevölkerung, die auf dem durch die Tschernobyl-Katastrophe verseuchten Territorium der Republik Belarus lebt. 1996, Minsk. Die wichtigsten Referate, Internat. Congress "The World after Tchernobyl", pp. 91-103.

Dubrova Y.E., Nesterov V.N., Krouchinsky N.G., Ostapenko V.A., Neumann R., Neil D.L. & Jeffreys A.J. : Human minisatellite mutation rate after the Chernobyl accident, Nature, 25 April 1996, Vol. 380, p 683-686.

Editorial : Children become the first victims of fallout. Science: vol. 272, 19 April 1996 pp. 357 à 360.

Fernex M. : Les conférences du 10e anniversaire de la catastrophe de Tchernobyl et le congrès de l'Agence International pour l'Energie Atomique (AIEA). Symposium "Tschernobyl, Projekte 1996", publié par l'Institut für Sozial- und Präventivmedizin der Universität Bern, Schweiz, P. Bleuer ed. 11. mai 1996, pp. 1-8.

Gadekar S. : Conclusion of the health survey of villages near Rawatbhata. CANE 767, 36 Cross, 4th Block Jayanagar Bangalore 560 041. April/May 1993 Anumukti Vol. 6 No 5, pp. 1-32.

Goncharova R.I. & Ryabokon N.I. : Proceedings : Belarus-

Japan Symposium "Acute and late Consequences of Nuclear Catastrophes: Hiroshima-Nagasaki and Chernobyl" Oct. 3-5, 1994. Belarus Academy of Sciences, Minsk.

Goncharova R.I. & Ryabokon N.I. : Dynamics of gamma-emitter content level in many generations of wild rodents in contaminated areas of Belarus. 2nd Intern. 25-26 October 1994, Conf. "Radiobiological Consequences of Nuclear Accidents".

Goncharova R.I. & Slukvin A.M. : Study on mutation and modification variability in young fishes of Cyprinus carpio from regions contaminated by the Chernobyl radioactive fallout. 27-28 October 1994, Russia-Norvegian Satellite Symposium on Nuclear Accidents, Radioecology and Health. Abstract Part 1, Moscow, 1994.

Gorpynchenko I.I & Boyko N.I. : Sexual disorders and generative function of males who took part in the liquidation of the consequences of the accident at the Chernobyl NPP, Book of extended Synopses, Austria Center Vienna, 8-12 April 1996, CN-63/264, pp. 389-390.

Hillis D.M. : Life in the hot zone around Chernobyl, Nature, 25 April 1996, Vol. 380, pp. 665-666.

Hug G.: Strahleninstitut. Proceedings, International conference : Chernobyl aid. June 18, 1994. München 1994.

International Perspectives in Public Health : Bhopal, vol. 11 & 12, 1996. IICPH, Toronto, Ontario, Canada.

Lalyzhev V.A. Pelevina I.I. Afanasief G.G., Gordienko S.M., Gubryi I.B., Klimenko T.I., Lukashova, R.G., Petrova I.V. & Sergeeva T.A.: Radiat. Biol. Ecol. 1993, Vol. 33, pp. 105-110.

Lazjuk G.I., Nikolajew D.L. & Nowikowa U.W. : Dynamik der angeborenen und vererbten Pathologien infolge der Katastrophe von Tschernobyl, In: "Die wichtigsten wissenschaftlichen Referate", 25-29 März 1996, Minsk. Internat. Congress "The World after Tchernobyl", pp. 123-131.

Lengfelder E. Institute of Radiobiology, University of Munich, personal comm., 1996.

Mangano J.J. : A post-Chernobyl rise in thyroid cancer in Connecticut, USA. European J. of Cancer Prevention, 1996, Vol. 5, pp. 75-81

Morgan K.Z. and Turner J.E. editor : "Principles of Radiation", N.Y. 1967.

Muller, H.J. : Genetics, Medicine and Man (1947)

Nesterenko W.B. : Ausmass der Folgen der Tschernobyl-Katastrophe in Belarus, Russland und der Ukraine. Minsk 1996 Belorussisches Institut für Strahlensicherheit "Belrad" Ed.: "Recht und Oekonomik" pp. 74, 1996.

Nussbaum R.H. & Köhnlein W. : Health consequences of exposures to ionizing radiation from external and internal sources : Challenges to radiation protection standards and biomedical research. Medicine and Global Survival Dec. 1995 Vol. 2, No 4, pp. 198 - 213.

Titov L.P., Kharitonic G., Gourmanchuk I.E. & Ignatenko S.I. : Effects of radiation on the production of immunoglobulins in children subsequent to the Chernobyl disaster. Allergy Proc. Vol. 16, No 4 July-August 1995 pp. 185-193.

Tsyb A.F, & Poverennyi A.M. : Damage of the thyroid in the period of the Chernobyl catastrophe: possible consequences. In "Consequences of the Chernobyl Catastrophe: Human Health", Ed.: E.B. Burlakova, Center for Russian Environmental Policy, Moscow, 1996, pp. 180-189.

Vassilevna T., Voitevich T., Mirkulova T., University Clinic of Pediatry, Minsk.1996. : personal comm.

Viel J.-F. : Conséquences des essais nucléaires sur la santé : quelles enquêtes épidémiologiques? Médecine et Guerre Nucléaire, janv.-mars 1996, Vol. 11, p 41-44. British Medical Journal, January 1997, vol. 314, p. 101-106.

Wolff Et. : Thesis on Teratology and X Rays, Arch. Anat. Hist. Embr. 1936, Vol. 22, pp. 1 - 382.

Books quoted during the hearing :

Bandahevsky Yu.I. and Lelevich V.V. : Clinical and experimental aspects of the effect of incorporated radionuclides upon the organism, Gomel, State Medical Institute, Belorussian Engineering Academy. Monograph of the Ministry of Health of the Republic of Belarus, pp. 128. 1995.

Belarus-Japan Symposium "Acute and late consequences of nuclear catastrophes : Hiroshima-Nagasaki and Chernobyl". Proceedings. Oct. 3-5, 1994

Belbéoch B. and Belbéoch R. : Tchernobyl, une catastrophe. Quelques éléments pour un bilan sept ans après. Edition Allia, 16 rue Charlemagne, Paris IVe , pp. 220. 1993.

Bertell Rosalie : No Immediate Danger : Prognosis for a Radioactive Earth. London : Women's Press, 1986.

Boos, Susan : Beherrschtes Entsetzen. Das Leben in der Ukraine zehn Jahre nach Tschernobyl. WoZ im Rotpunktverlag,. Druck : Fuldaer Verlagsanstalt, Fulda, Deutschland. ISBN 3-85869-162-3, 1996.

Burlakova E.B. Editor: Consequences of the Chernobyl Catastrophe : Human Health. Center for Russian Environmental Policy. Scientific Council on Radiobiology Russian Academy of Sciences, pp. 250. Moscow 1996.

Busby C. : Wings of Death. Nuclear pollution and Human Health. Green Audit (Wales) Ltd. Aberystwyth, Publication Department, 38 Queen Street, Aberystwyth, Dyfed, SY23 1PU, United Kingdom. 1995

Ford D.S. : Three Mile Island. Thirty Minutes to Meltdown. Penguin Books pp. 271, 1981, 1982.

Gould Jay, & Mangano J. : The Enemy Within. The high cost of living near nuclear reactors", Four Walls Eight Windows Ed. (1996)

Graeub R. : Der Petkau-Effekt. Katastrophale Folgen niedriger Radioaktivität. Tatsachen und Befürchtungen. Zytglogge Verlag Wien, Strozzigasse 14-16. A-1080 Wien. pp. 250. ISBN3 7296 0365 5. 1990.

Gruschewoj G. : Die wichtigsten Referate, Internat. Congress "The World after Tchernobyl", pp. 91-103. Minsk, 25-29 März, 1996.

Konoplya E.F. & Rolevich I.V. Ed. : The Chernobyl Catastrophe consequences in the Republic of Belarus, Ministry for Emergencies and Population Protection from the Chernobyl NPP Catastrophe Consequences, Academy of Sciences of Belarus, Minsk 1996.

Makhijani A and Makhijani Annie : Fissile Materials in a Glass, darkly. Technical and Policy Aspects of the Disposition of Plutonium and Highly Enriched Uranium. IEER Press. Institute for Energy and Environmental Research. 6935 Laurel Avenue, Takoma Park, Maryland 20912. 1995.

Nesterenko W.B. : "Ausmass und Folgen der Tschernobyl-Katastrophe in Belarus, Russland und der Ukraine. Recht und Ökonomik, pp. 73 , 1996.

Roche Adi, : Children of Chernobyl. The Human Cost of the World's worst Nuclear Disaster. An Onprint of Harper Collins Publisher, 77-85 Fulham Palace Road, London W6 8JB, 1996

Schuchardt Erika und Kopelew L. : Die Stimmen der Kinder von Tschernobyl. Geschichte einer stillen Revolution. Herder. Freiburg . Basel . Wien . Herder/Spektrum Band 4476. pp. 189. 1996.

Stscherbak J.: Protokolle einer Katastrophe (Aus dem Russischen von Barbara Conrad) Athenäum Verlag GmbH. Die kleine weisse Reihe. Frankfurt am Main 1988.

Weizsäcker von E.U., Lovins Amory B. und Lovins L.H : Faktor Vier. Doppelter Wohlstand- halbierter Naturverbrauch. Der neue Beriche an den CLUB OF ROME. Droemer Knaur Verlagsanstalt München, pp. 352, 1995.

Yarochinskaya Alla : Tchernobyl; Vérité interdite (traduit du russe par Michèle Kahn). Published with the help of the Green Group in the European Parliament, Ed de l'Aube, pp. 143; 1993.

Glossary :

- Becquerel : A measure of radioactivity of a substance equalling one disintegration per second. One Becquerel equals about 27 picoCurie

- Curie : A measure of radioactivity of a substance equalling 37 billion disintegrations per second. This is the traditional measure of radioactivity and is based on the number of disintegrations per second undergone by one gram of pure radium-226. One Curie equals 37 billion Becquerels.

- Gray : A unit of radiation dose equal to 100 rads.

- Milli- : Prefix used with rads, rems, Gray, Sievert and other units to indicate one-thousandth part of the unit.

- Micro- : Prefix used with rads rems, Gray, Sievert and other units to indicate one-millionth part of the unit.

- Nano - : Prefix used with rads, rems, Gray, Sievert and other units to indicate one-billionth part of the unit.

- Pico- : Prefix used with rads rems, Gray, Sievert and other units to indicate one-trillionth part of the unit.

- Rad : A unit of dose equal to the deposition of 100 ergs of energy per gram of material being irradiated.

- Rem : A unit of dose that takes into account the relative biological damage due to various kinds of radiation energy absorbed by tissues.

- Sievert : A unit of effective dose equal to 100 rems.

Judgement of the Tribunal

1. THE PROCEDURE :

The request for a Session on the environmental, health and human rights implications of the Chernobyl disaster was presented in late 1995 by the "International Medical Commission on Chernobyl" (IMCC) in response to growing medical, scientific and human rights concerns over the extraordinarily narrow definition of "damage to health" and "certainty of knowledge" being used by the international nuclear community to describe the aftermath of the Chernobyl disaster.

According to its statutes, the PPT notified the acceptance of the request, as well as the timing and modalities of the procedures of the session, to the United Nations (UN), the European Union (EU), the World Health Organisation (WHO), the International Atomic Energy Agency (IAEA), and the International Commission on Radiological Protection (ICRP). A prompt answer and a set of pertinent documentation was received from the Department of Humanitarian Affairs of the UN; an answer requesting to be informed on the results of the session from WHO; a note proposing the postponement of the hearings of the Tribunal "after the result of the Conference in Vienna (8-12 April) have become available" from the IAEA. Experts and witnesses presented oral as well as written evidence to the PPT, and were available for answering the questions of the Judges :

The Permanent People's Tribunal Judges :

M. Francois Rigaux	President of the Permanent People's Tribunal Professor of International Law, Louvain-la-Neuve, Belgium
M. Elmar Altvater	Professor of Economics, Free University, Berlin,
Ms. Freda Meissner-Blau	President of Ecoropa, Vienna, Austria
M. Surendar Gadekar	Nuclear Physicist, Vedcchi, India
Ms. Corinne Kumar	Sociologist, Asian Women's Human Rights, Council, India/Tunis
M. Mitsuo Okamoto	Professor, Peace Studies, Hiroshima Shudo University, Japan

The Program :

1. INTRODUCTION TO TESTIMONIES :

- Dr Gianni Tognoni, Secretary General of the Permanent People's Tribunal (PPT), Italy : History of the Permanent People's Tribunal, and its concern for human rights of victims of industrial and technological disasters.
- Dr. Rosalie Bertell, Co-ordinator of the International Medical Commission Chernobyl (IMCC) Canada : Questions before the Tribunal on the Chernobyl disaster.

2. THE ACCIDENT AND ITS IMPLICATIONS FOR OTHER NUCLEAR REACTORS AND FOR DEVELOPING COUNTRIES :

- Sergii Mirnyi, Engineer, Physico-Chemist, Director on Science and International Relations for the International Poster and Graphics Exhibition dedicated to Chernobyl : The nature of the disaster, and its effects on water, soil and air.
- Professor Vesily Nesterenko, Belarussian Research Technical Centre, Institute of Radiation Safety, Head for Belarus of the Independent Expert Committee Three State Inquiry into the Consequences of the Chernobyl Disaster : Monitoring the contaminated food.

206

- Commander Robert Green, Royal Navy (Retired) : The implications of the explosion of Chernobyl Reactor 4 for western nuclear power plants.
- Professor Jouli Andreev, one of the main leaders of the Liquidators.
- Dr. Wolfgang Kromp, Nuclear Advisor of the Austrian Federal Chancellor.
- Professor Ross Hesketh, Berkeley Nuclear Laboratory of the Central Generating Board CEGB (retired).

3. CHERNOBYL AND THE HUMAN RIGHTS OF THE VICTIMS :

- Dr. Irina Groushevaya, The Chernobyl Children Foundation, Minsk : The medical, ecological and sociological situation and the responses of governments and international agencies.
- Dr. Youri Pankratz, The Chernobyl Children Foundation, Minsk : The medical, ecological and sociological situation and the responses of governments and international agencies.
- Prof Galina A Drozdova, Russian People's Friendship University, Moscow. On the decade after Chernobyl: information deficiency and socio-medical problems.
- Prof Larissa Skuratovskaya, Institute of General Pathology and Pathophysiology, Russian Academy of Medical Sciences : Human rights, the death penalty, nuclear weapons and health issues in Russia.
- Professor Peter Weish, Member of the Austrian Academy of Science.
- Prof Hari Sharma, Nuclear Chemistry, University of Waterloo, Canada, IMCC.

4. EVIDENCE OF GENETIC OR TERATOGENIC DAMAGE TO THE ENVIRONMENT AND HUMANS :

Ms. Cornelia Hesse-Honegger, Scientific Illustrator specialising in Zoology, : Insects collected from Chernobyl, Sellafield and near Swiss nuclear power plants.
- Ms. Solange Fernex, former Member of the European Parliament : Video-tape presentation of deformities in plants, animal fetuses and children, following the Chernobyl catastrophe.
- Dr Sanghamitra Gadekar, IMCC : Experiences near a nuclear reactor in India.

5. DIRECT DAMAGE TO PEOPLE ATTRIBUTABLE TO CHERNOBYL:

- Professor E. B. Burlakova, Semenov Institute of Chemical Physics, Russian Academy of Sciences, Moscow : low intensity radiation : radio-biological aspects.
- Professor Yvetta N. Kogarko, Semenov Institute of Chemical Physics, Russian Academy of Sciences, Moscow : Monitoring and features of lymphoproliferative diseases in people living in the zone of radiation pollution after the accident at Chernobyl.
- Professor Irina I. Pelevina, Semenov Institute of Chemical Physics, Russian Academy of Sciences, Moscow : Experimental results from Chernobyl area on blood lymphocytes in adults and children living in contaminated areas.
- Professor Ludmilla Kryzhanovskaya, Chief of the Department, Kiev Institute of Social and Forensic Psychiatry : Mental disorders among Chernobyl survivors.
- Professor Leonid Titov, Director of the Research Institute for Epidemiology, Immunology and Microbiology of Belarus, Minsk : Immune system of children and Chernobyl.
- Professor Nika Gres, Research Institute of Radiation Medicine, Minsk, Belarus : Children residing on radioactive contaminated land.
- Professor Jay Gould, President of the Radiation and Public Health Project, New York : Effects of Chernobyl in North America.
- Professor Inge Schmitz-Feuerhake, Medical Physics, University of Bremen, Germany, IMCC.
- Dr. Andreas Nidecker, Medical Radiologist, Post-President of PSR/IPPNW, Basle, Switzerland, IMCC.

6. THE JAPANESE EXPERIENCE AT HIROSHIMA AND NAGASAKI :

Dr. Katsumi Furitsu, Internist, Investigative Committee of Atomic Bombing Victims, Hannan Chuo Hospital, Osaka, Japan : The parallel radiation injuries of the atomic bombing victims in Hiroshima and Nagasaki after 50 years, and the Chernobyl victims after 10 years.
Ms. Kazuko Yamashina, Nagasaki Survivor, Chernobyl Relief Group of Kansai, Japan.
Dr. Sanghamitra Gadekar, IMCC : Experiences near a nuclear reactor in India.
Dr. Kazue Sadamori, Pharmacist, Investigative Committee

of Atomic Bombing Victims, Hannan Chuo Hospital, Osaka, Japan.

7. RESPONSES OF NATIONAL AND INTERNATIONAL AGENCIES:

- Dr. Vladimir Iakimets, Institute for Systems Analysis of the Russian Academy of Sciences, and Board Member of the Nevada-Semipalatinsk Movement : Decade after Chernobyl, knowledge gained against impact revision.
- Dr Katsumi Furitsu, Investigative Committee of Atomic Bombing Victims at Hannan Chuo Hospital : The Japanese experience with the International Commission on Radiological Protection (ICRP) and the International Atomic Energy Agency (IAEA).
- Prof. Michel Fernex University of Basle, Switzerland : Reporting on the World Health Organisation Conference : "On the Health Consequences of the Chernobyl and Other Radiological Accidents", 20-23 Nov. 1995; the Third Annual NGO Conference in Minsk 23-29 March 1996, "The World After Chernobyl", and the International Atomic Energy Conference in Vienna 8-12 April 1996, "One Decade After Chernobyl: Summing up the Consequences of the Accident".

8. CONCLUSIONS:

- Ms. Nuala Ahern, Member of the European Parliament : On the IAEA Conference.
- Dr. Rosalie Bertell : The International Medical Commission on Chernobyl.

* * * *

The PPT also had the opportunity to examine the following written documentation :

- The Helsinki Declaration on Action for Environment and Health in Europe, 1994.

- WHO, International Programme on the Health Effects of the Chernobyl Accident, Report by the Director General, 27/2/1995.

- WHO Health Consequences of the Chernobyl Accident-Results of the IPHECA pilot projects and related national programmes, Summary Report, 1995.

- UNSCEAR, Effects of Radiation on the Environment, 17/2/1995

- NEA-OECD, Chernobyl : Ten Years on. Radiological and Health Impact. An appraisal by the NEA Committee on Radiation Protection and Public Health, November 1995

- EU-IAEA-WHO, Documentation for the International Conference, "One Decade After Chernobyl : Summing up the Consequences of the Accident" (Vienna 8-12 April 1996).

Working Material :

- One Decade after Chernobyl : Environmental Impact and Prospects For the Future, IAEA Conference 8 - 12 March 1996, Vienna, Background Papers to Sessions 5, 7, 8, Book of Extended Synopses, Statements of the President of the Republic of Belarus and of the Prime Minister of Ukraine, Closing Session: Keynote closing remarks and keynote statements presenting the final conclusions and recommendation of the IAEA Conference, Friday 12 April 1996, 12.30 hr.
- International Congress "The World After Chernobyl", Main Scientific Reports, Minsk, March 1996.

Books :

- Nesterenko V.B., : Scales and Consequences of the Disaster at the Chernobyl NPP for Belarus, Russia and Ukraine, Minsk 1996.
- Adi Roche : Children of Chernobyl, the human cost of the world's worst nuclear disaster, Fount Ed, 1996.
- Schuchardt E, Kopelew L, : Die Stimmen der Kinder von Tchernobyl. Geschichte einer stillen Revolution, Herder 1996.
- Gould, J., : The Enemy Within, the high cost of living near nuclear reactors, Four Walls Eight Windows, Ed, 1996.
- Susan Boos : Beherrschtes Entsetzen, Zytglogge, 1996.

For their deliberations the Judges also took into account the jurisdiction of the previous verdicts of the PPT (see below) and their detailed references into the documents and conventions of international law.

Specific attention has been given to the Conventions on the Limitations of Liability for Nuclear Accidents.

2. THE LINK OF THIS SESSION TO THE PREVIOUS JURISDICTION OF THE PPT

The most immediate connection must be obviously traced to the verdict on Industrial Hazards and Human Rights (London, December 1994), which concluded a series of hearings, one of which was specifically dedicated to the Bhopal Disaster (Bhopal, 1992).

The violation of the right of the victims of "accidents" to life, health, information, compensation, was explicitly seen as the expression of the broader and deeper aggression, which is waged against its least protected members by a society, which respects economic rules and interests much more than fundamental human rights.

The mechanisms, the means and the actors of this aggression have been analysed in depth in the Sessions dedicated to the Policies of the International Monetary Fund and World Bank (Berlin 1988, Madrid, 1994). On the other side, the failure of the existing international law provisions and instruments, to protect adequately the rights of the victims, has been the specific focus of the series of hearings, the Verdict on Impunity for Crimes Against Humanity (Bogota, 1991) and the special Session on the Conquest of America and International Law (Padua, Venice, 1992).

This last verdict underlined very strongly the insufficiency of the present system of international relations, to provide protection and promotion of fundamental rights of peoples, and the challenges it must face of democratising its institutions and broadening the base of its authority, to the domain of economic and more generally, development-related relationships (see Verdict of Madrid, 1994, quoted above), where the new "low intensity" wars are waged, and peoples rights are denied or violated.

The deep implications of this perspective have been further explored and documented in the Session dedicated to the Violations of the Rights of Children (Naples, April 4, 1995), as they have been specifically affirmed in the UN Convention of 1990. Breeches of the fundamental rights of those who represent the future of humanity, recall very closely the scenario of the Chernobyl disaster, where the reproductive rights and possibilities are directly threatened, and the severe children morbidity has broken the barrier of silence and denial, which had appeared to be the rule in the official international public scene.

3. FACTS

a) Causes of the Chernobyl Disaster :

The principle immediate cause of this disaster was the design flaw in the RBMK-type 950 MW nuclear reactor, which caused a dramatic power surge when the operators attempted to shut down the reactor, and a subsequent nuclear explosion. This design flaw was known prior to the disaster, and had been officially noted on at least two occasions in the Soviet Union prior to April 1986.

At the time of the disaster, about 800,000 workers were drafted to assist in emergency response. They lacked basic training in radiation safety, had no access to self-protective measures, and no informed consent procedure was followed. Workers were exposed to high doses of radiation, and nuclear fallout was widespread, both locally and throughout Europe and beyond.

There was delay in informing the people at risk, in the former Soviet Union, Europe and the world, of the seriousness of the accident. Little protective response for the general population, especially children and pregnant women, was undertaken, and citizens were allowed to participate, for example, in the May Day Parades out of doors, during a time of dangerous radioactive fallout.

Officially, responsibility for the disaster was attributed to the plant operators, and little public blame fell on the designers and regulators, who failed to deal with known flaws in the reactor. The true nature of the nuclear explosion was not admitted publicly, and the implications for all other nuclear reactors in the world was played down. Although much of the popular explanation of the widespread devastation was attributed to the lack of a containment for the nuclear reactor, this may have acted as a benefit, a relief valve which prevented a worse explosion.

b) Consequences of the Disaster

The disaster killed 31 people immediately, caused about 130,000 acute radiation exposures, and the evacuation and relocation of hundreds of thousands of people. Some of the most severe long term effects were related to the nuclear contamination of the soil, crops, sediment and water. The nuclear radiation, in particulate form, was stored in the tissues and bones of the people and the food chain, posing a threat to life and health which continues to the present time, ten years after the disaster.

Due to the investigations of the World Health Organisation, we now know that at least 700 cases of thyroid cancers in young children and adolescents, have resulted from the radioactive Iodine inhalation, with ten known deaths. There have been further problems, especially among the children, with other thyroid diseases including Hashimoto thyroiditis, with blood abnormalities, anemia, gastro-intestinal disorders, juvenile diabetes, and immune system dysfunction.

Social disruption, relocation, loss of jobs and homes, illness and fear, have contributed to problems of adaptation to life since the disaster. A new syndrome, called by a Ukrainian physician, "Post Chernobyl Cerebrasthenic Syndrome", which affected large numbers of survivors of the disaster, caused symptoms such as poor attention, fatigue, short term memory loss, irritability, dizziness and fatigue, high sensitivity to loud noise, bright lights and high temperature. A physician familiar with Hiroshima and Nagasaki survivors noted the similarity of this syndrome with an atomic bomb survivor illness, called "Genbaku Bura Bura".

Although the existence of many non-lethal effects of radiation exposure is admitted by the International Commission on Radiological Protection (ICRP), these effects are not deemed by the regulatory committees to be "of concern" to society. The ICRP, in its history since 1952, has recognised "radiation-induced fatal cancers" and what it designates to be "serious genetic disease in live-born offspring" to be the only recognised medical effects of radiation exposure of concern. Since Chernobyl, the recognition of non-fatal thyroid cancer especially in children, and severe mental retardation resulting from exposure of the fetuses in the 8-15 first weeks of intrauterine life, has been officially admitted. However, much evidence of the harm caused by a variety of mutations, cellular disruptions and intra-uterine damages, including all levels of mental retardation, physical disabilities including deformed or absent arms and legs, blindness and deafness, were demonstrated by witnesses to have occurred to plants, animals and humans. It was obvious that these severe sufferings for the affected individuals, their families, communities, life supporting environment and food web, were of major concern to the victims. The administrative absence of concern for these real outcomes of radiation exposure, was in itself one of the ways in which the victims were revictimised after the disaster.

c) Compensation

The questions of compensation for the victims of the disaster are closely connected with the identification of the causes of the disaster, the responsible agents and the legitimate medical claims. The causes are imbedded in military and industrial policies and designs, engineering assumptions and even development models. Responsibility rested with local operators, national regulators and international recommending agencies like the ICRP, the International Atomic Energy Agency (IAEA), and several United Nations (UN) Agencies. It was the international recommending body, ICRP, which strictly limited the recognition of medical ills attributable to the radiation exposure, and these recommendations were strictly enforced, against the advice of local physicians and health professionals actually dealing with the victims.

Because of disputes over which illnesses should be recognised for compensation, between those working with the victims and regulatory agencies which define what illnesses should be "of concern", the international community has been slow to come to the assistance of the victims. In Belarus 25% of the government budget goes to restorations of Chernobyl devastation.

The most recent approach to rehabilitation, both in Russia and Belarus was the proposal to raise the permissible levels of nuclear pollution in soil, especially outside the constructed areas, relocation of the population on contaminated land, and relaxing the standards for nuclear contamination of food and water. So-called unoccupied land is agricultural, and use of contaminated land for food production can be expected to produce new radiation victims, and to worsen both the health and reproductive capacity of current radiation victims. These new policies appear to have been derived from a new policy of the ICRP, proposed in its document No 60, 1990, which states that after a nuclear accident ALARA (as low as reasonably achievable) policy no longer applies. The new policy requires that risk-benefit studies should be done for evacuation, restricted use of land or consumption of food, or other radiation protection activities. The recommendations of the IAEA appear to be an enforcement of this ICRP policy recommendation.

This new policy impacts on the compensation question, and on the mitigation of the results of a serious disaster, by limiting clean-up policy, and by forcing the population to accept unhealthy living conditions and contaminated food and water, in the name of economic efficiency. The burden of proof is shifted on the victim, who needs now to justify clean-up, rather than on the polluter. We must ensure that it is the perpetrators who must assume the burden of restoring, as far as possible, the health of the victims and the integrity of the environment, which they have severely damaged.

4. COVER-UP BY THE INTERNATIONAL COMMUNITY

The beginnings of the nuclear age were shrouded in secrecy, because of the fear of the spread of knowledge of nuclear technology, and retaliation for use of the atomic bomb against Japan in World War II. Physicists, because of their skill in measuring radiation, assume also the job of predicting the results of exposure. Prior to WW II, medical radiologists had understood some of the devastating effects of exposure to the X-ray, and had formed an international radiologist association to set occupational and safety criteria for its use. Physicists from the Manhattan Project, the WW II atomic bomb project, from the US, UK and Canada met together between 1945 and 1952, to determine recommendations for radiation protection, in view of this new technology, of atmospheric weapons testing which began in the Pacific Atoll of Bikini in 1946, and proposed expansion of uranium mining and other weapon related industries. In 1952, these physicists joined the radiologists, and formed the ICRP. Because of the nuclear secrecy, this association was established as, and has continued to be self-appointed and self-perpetuating in membership. It has always claimed to assess both the hazards and the benefits of radiation use, making what it believed to be rational trade-off of risks for benefits.

Membership in ICRP has consisted of users of radiation, about 50% physicists and 15% radiologists, with medical administrators making up about 25% and 10% from a scattering of disciplines. The results of ICRP deliberations and recommendations have been standard settings for occupational and public health exposures to radiation which they found acceptable to accommodate the new technology (and atmospheric weapon testing). Their recommendations were widely accepted by national regulatory bodies, and generally implemented internationally. The findings of the US investigations of the atomic bomb victims in Hiroshima and Nagasaki, and the UK studies of patients who received high therapeutic doses of radiation for a spinal disease, have been the fundamental studies, which justified ICRP recommendations. All other radiation research must "harmonise" with these studies in order to be admitted into the regulatory base. Both of these examples involve high doses of radiation, delivered in a short period of time. Limited biological endpoints were studied, primarily fatal cancers, and extrapolation of these findings to exposures to low doses, extended over long periods of time, (such as would be experienced by workers and the public) was attempted.

Expertise in public or occupational health has not been represented on the Main Committee of ICRP, which makes all decisions.

After the 1954 explosion of the hydrogen bomb, and the decision of the US to convert its arsenal to nuclear devices, the "Peaceful Atom" program was introduced into the UN, and the International Atomic Energy Agency (IAEA) was established. The IAEA was mandated to promote "peaceful" uses of nuclear technology, and to prevent nuclear military technology from expanding into countries other than the five nations then known to have developed it. In this promotional role, IAEA has depended on the recommendations of the ICRP for its radiation protection standards.

The UN also established a committee called the UN Scientific Committee on the Effects of Atomic Radiation (UNSCEAR), which periodically reports to the General Assembly on new research or policies coming from the ICRP or IAEA.

This system of agencies is very tightly knitted, with many overlapping memberships. It has been effectively isolated from normal channels of occupational and public health, which deal with chemical pollutants and other industrial hazards. Specialities in scientific training have also worked

216

to isolate the nuclear agencies from general medical and scientific scrutiny. For example, while the nuclear industry has continued to base its recommendations on "fatal cancers", the chemical industries have been forced to look at respiratory illnesses, neurotoxic effects in children, in-utero disruption of growth and development as biological endpoints.

Attendance at meetings of the IAEA, and staff positions require that the individuals have a recommendation from the nuclear regulatory agency of their UN member country. The ICRP appoints its own membership and appointment has no time limit. Members of UNSCEAR serve at the pleasure of their national governments, most of which have nuclear programs. This small group of scientists has full control of policy making, and of recognition given to "outside" research, which may challenge its findings and decisions. All who disagree with the recommendations and policies, are labelled either ignorant, emotional or non-scientific. There is no international forum in which disputes can be resolved, either for scientific questions or for policy decisions.

5. RESPONSIBILITY OF THE SCIENTIFIC COMMUNITY

Members of the scientific community within the nuclear community, find it difficult to freely discuss differences of interpretation of scientific data, or differences in policy decisions, because of their continued membership in the organisations. Often their livelihood are at stake. For example, if an organisation such as the WHO could place a member on the ICRP, then that member could speak on public health policy in keeping with WHO policy without threat to their membership. Currently, members of ICRP serve at the choice of the ICRP Executive Committee.

Scientists outside of the nuclear community have found it difficult to obtain grant money for research. The medical community dealing with nuclear exposure victims, have little say in the establishment of research needs, and in directing money to research independent of the nuclear industry. Because of the control exerted over research goals and financial allocation, the victims often are left without the information needed to prove causal relationships between exposure and illness. Research which is completed, must pass through a review process, prior to publication. Often these papers are sent for review to pronuclear experts, who refuse publication to those findings, which appear to contradict the prevailing wisdom.

The complexity of the nuclear questions, and the need for interdisciplinary approaches to most problems it poses, makes research in this field expensive. Institutional support for interdisciplinary teams is essential. Communication of results should be widespread in order to conserve resources.

The Tribunal commends those scientists and physicians who have tried to speak for the public good, both within and outside of the nuclear circles. Yet it notes the lack of democratic sharing and the severe penalties against speaking out in contradiction of the prevailing "truth", which is essentially detrimental to the public good. In a special way, because of the secrecy of the nuclear beginnings, and the extraordinary control of policy-related information in this field, the structural hindrance of professional interaction is extraordinarily effective. It was reported that at the IAEA meeting in Vienna this April, scientists who had spoken at a prior meeting in Minsk a week ago, failed to speak up with respect to findings and data in their possession. This intimidation of scientists undermines the just response to the disaster, and the addressing of the human rights of the victims.

6. NUCLEAR WEAPONS AND NUCLEAR POWER PLANTS

Half a century after the atomic bombings of Hiroshima and Nagasaki, and a decade after the nuclear power plant disaster at Chernobyl, comprehensive scientific and medical evidence has sufficiently proven that survivors, especially women and children, of the atomic bombings and nuclear power plants accidents, suffer from diverse, yet almost identical, psycho-somatic diseases and congenital deformities, hitherto unknown to humanity in this amount.

The world needs to hear the voices of victims of uranium mining, nuclear power plant operation, clean-up operations, waste disposal, the nuclear weapons production complex, and nuclear weapons testing sites, numbering at least 32 million, who cry out for relief from the ills of this doomsday technology.

The magnitude of global contamination of soil, water, and

air, already caused by the Chernobyl disaster and likely to be caused again by nuclear war, and/or nuclear power plant accidents, pose horrendous menace, not only to the existing life and health of people on earth, but are threatening to render the ecosystem totally irreparable for an indefinite future, and thus deprive the most basic human rights of the future generations.

The world-wide spread of Plutonium and its easy convertibility into nuclear weapons, has made increasing inroads into the control of information and the suppression of democracy.

The military atom and the civilian atom are two sides of the same coin, and the existence of the one reinforces the other. It is inevitable, therefore, that the spread of commercial nuclear technology will result in the further spread of nuclear weapons, abrogating even the limited fruits of the NPT and CTBT.

France and China, which have recently conducted nuclear weapons testing, against the international public opinion, must realise that they have not only made a grave political mistake in the Post Cold War period, where the theory of deterrence has categorically lost its credibility, but also encouraged some countries to obtain nuclear weapons capability.

7. THE LAW OF RESPONSIBILITY AND OF COMPENSATION

Two questions have to be separated from one another :

- Who is liable and for what?
- How can damage be compensated?

1. The law of liability

According to a tradition, upon which civil law countries and common law systems do coincide - in spite of differences which are not relevant here - one is liable for the damage he or she has inflicted upon another person. The same principles apply to state responsibility, according to international law, which is drawn from general principles of law. Such a system of liability is based on the principle of causation : along with the progress of natural sciences, which identifies links between two observable phenomena, the one being the cause or the antecedent of others (the effects), judges have held liable the agent whose activity has been harmful to another person. Such an application of the juridical principle of causation combines three elements :

- 1) a damage has to be identified;
- 2) a wrong has been committed;
- 3) there exists a causal link between the wrongful act and the damage.

However simple this scheme seems to be, its application has raised considerable difficulties and many theories have been imagined to reconcile the difficulty to know what really occurred, with the requirements of judiciary practice. The two main theories aiming at selecting within the almost infinite field of antecedents, those which are retained as relevant for the lawyer's purpose, are the theory of proximate causation (usual in common law), and in civil law countries, the theory of adequate causation (Adequanztheorie).

Before contemplating the supplementary difficulties which arise in the field of nuclear damages, one has to add two elements : the proximate causation implies an element which can be foreseen. To be liable, the agent had to be aware that his or her conduct put another person at risk. But it is not necessary that a high degree of probability be demonstrated. If I drive on an isolated road, where the circulation is very scarce, it is highly improbable that at the time I pass another vehicle, a third one will arrive from the opposite direction. However, I am at fault if I assume such a risk. The second element to stress is that liability can be engaged through omissions as well as through action. If someone enters into a dangerous activity, they are under duty of taking any safety measures to prevent foreseeable harm. The application of such principles to nuclear nuisances, will meet with two series of difficulties.

a)   Low-level radiation falls out of the scope of the principle of causation, which is built on the correlation of two events. A damage which is the consequences of low-level exposure, cannot be detected before a long lapse of time, and it can be related to anyone among the many influences and deficiencies to which a person has been subjected. The experience has been made with professional diseases. Since they could not be compensated according to the traditional principle of causation, statutes have been passed, which provided for a strict liability system : in each branch of industry which can generate a professional disease, the workmen are afforded a system of lump sum compensation.

b)   The traditional rules of liability could have been applied to the Chernobyl tragedy, as they should have been to the Bhopal disaster, and the Tribunal has to investigate why they were ruled out. It is very symptomatic that the responsibility for nuclear accidents seems to be put beyond the boundaries of a law-abiding society. Neither were the victims of the Three Mile Island accident compensated, although the American case law is among the most generous for other kinds of victims. In the numerous proceedings for product liability, the unduly rigorous standard of evidence, which are deemed acceptable for the experts of the International Atomic Energy Agency, is not paramount. The thalidomide case is a clear example at hand. Even if the victim's ailment can also have another cause, it is sufficient that a statistical correlation demonstrates the link between the local apparition of a damage and with the conduct which has caused it, to conclude to the liability.

In the case of Chernobyl the apparition of ailments in a group of persons exposed to the radiation which statistically exceeded the dispersion of the same illness in a population which was not within the field of irradiation, would suffice to engage the liability of the radiation. One cannot require a supplementary evidence as to the previous health conditions of the contaminated population.

2. Damage which cannot be compensated

The magnitude of the damage explains - but it does not justify - why they cannot be duly compensated. It is no coincidence that the two worst industrial catastrophes, Bhopal and Chernobyl, occurred in places where human life has not the price it is evaluated through American or Western-European standards. Should such a disaster have occurred in Germany, or in the United States, the whole insurance system would have collapsed. The methods followed after Chernobyl to assess the damages, which are deemed acceptable by the "experts" of the IAEA, were not conceived in order to provide for a just or fair compensation to the victims, human suffering was negated or squeezed, for the reparations to remain within payment capabilities and expectations. Not only were the victims not

221

compensated, but the reality of the harm they were subjected to and their sufferings have been denied, because compensation did not enter into the scheme of the so-called rationality of nuclear energy. Every fact, which could be put to blame the atomic energy complex, had to be disregarded. That complex is above the law, it has built within and around the nuclear plants, a no-law's land.

8. ECONOMIC ASPECTS OF NUCLEAR ENERGY PRODUCTION

1. Unaccountable risks

The times of the illusion that "atomic energy for peace" may resolve the energy problem of humankind are over, at least since the nuclear accident of Three Mile Island and the disaster of Chernobyl. Nevertheless, production of nuclear energy continues, and there are powerful economic interests in favour of nuclear energy, exerting pressure on political decision-makers as well as on the public. The danger of a major accident in one of the several hundred nuclear power stations in nearly all parts of the globe, the promoters of nuclear energy say, is banned. But it is not only this danger which creates preoccupation of people in the world. It is the whole production chain of nuclear energy, from extraction of uranium to the disposal of nuclear waste. Since the beginning of the nuclear age, an unaccounted number of miners have been contaminated, as well as workers in processing the ore in uranium plants, and in the power plants, or the nuclear waste disposals. None of these links of the nuclear chain is safe in terms of minor or major accidents, or with regard to the ubiquitous low-dose radiation. The risks are incalculable, especially in the case of waste disposals, because future generations are concerned. They cannot announce their priorities on the present market. This is a clear case of market failures. Calculations made up by representatives of the nuclear industry, or the IAEA demonstrating economic advantages of nuclear energy compared to other sources of energy, therefore, cannot be taken seriously. They are irresponsible, since they play down the extremely high "external diseconomies" of nuclear energy.

The quotation of M. Hans Blix, should it be correct (Le Monde 28.8.1986), displays even more than irresponsibility : "due to the importance of this energy, the world could support one accident of the Chernobyl scale every year...". The "value" of a human being, its life, integrity and health, obviously count economically for nothing. But this inhuman attitude seems to be a necessary prerequisite for continuing the strategy of producing atomic energy, even after Chernobyl. Victims are the price of progress.

2. Opportunity costs of nuclear energy

Therefore it is quite logical that the IAEA, ten years after the disaster of Chernobyl, criminally plays down the number of lethal victims to a regrettable number of 31 or 32 (less than in a major air accident), although serious scientists from concerned Eastern European countries as well as from Western research institutions, are counting more than 25,000 people killed immediately in the course of the disaster or dying due to the effects of the explosion during the past decade, not to speak about hundred thousands of people being injured and contaminated from the local population to the "liquidators", concentrated in the area of the disaster from the whole territory of the former Soviet Union. The attempts of reconstructing the acceptability and trust for nuclear energy production, seems to be of much more importance, than taking into consideration the long term effects of radiation on future generations, due to possible genetic mutations. The same neglect happens in the case of the opportunity costs (lacking means for schooling, infrastructure, welfare etc.), since more than 25% of the state budget of a poor country like Belarus, has to be devoted to the containment of the effects of the Chernobyl disaster. Summing up all costs of the disaster, the production of atomic energy is not at all an economical solution to the energy problem of modern societies.

3. Nuclear energy is no alternative to fossil energies in order to avoid the greenhouse effect.

It is said that the use of fossil energies creates so many negative effects that for many decades, nuclear energy will remain a rational alternative. Firstly, in the next century fossil sources probably will be exhausted and, secondly and even more important, they have to be substituted even before running out, because of the greenhouse effect. Moreover, the international community committed itself to a remarkable reduction of CO_2 emissions in the next two decades. The reduction of CO_2 emissions is absolutely necessary, but no excuse for the continued use of nuclear energy. It is no alternative to fossil energy, as it again has been suggested in the final declaration of the IAEA conference on Chernobyl in Vienna in April 1996.

Apart from the ecological and human costs of nuclear energy, the economic costs are much too high, in the case that they are internalised into the price formation of electricity produced by nuclear power stations. This is a reason why many highly developed countries in the meanwhile stopped the construction of new nuclear plants, and why less developed countries in planning nuclear power plants, do not fully take into consideration full costs.

Moreover, there are still other well known negative impacts of atomic energy on mankind. Nuclear energy cannot be "democratised". It is too dangerous in terms of risk management, too prone to terrorist attacks and it is too simple to transform a nuclear power plant into a nuclear weapon plant. The more countries utilise nuclear power plants, the greater the jeopardy for peace in the world.

4. The necessity of an alternative energy model

Since nuclear energy is no alternative to fossil energies, and sources of fossil energies can only be used to a diminishing degree, it is of utmost importance for humankind to develop an alternative energy model. It must be based firstly, on a considerable increase of energy efficiency and on technical and social methods of avoiding and saving energy, and secondly, on a strategy of transition from fossil and nuclear energy to renewable, non exhaustible solar energy.

On both paths, technical and social progress already takes place. There exist already technologies to increase energy efficiency in all parts of the world, adapted to different climatic, geographical, and social conditions. The willingness to change lifestyles is growing even in the rich countries, a precondition for improving the energy situation in the poor parts of the world. Alternative energies are better for a decentralised and diversified consumption and production model, than fossil and nuclear energies, which exert a powerful territorial agglomeration effect and economic concentration effects.

5. Political tasks of supporting an alternative energy model.

It is one of the main tasks of political leadership to support and promote alternatives to the prevailing energy model, even against the lagging and cushioning interests of big corporations and the economic-scientific complex. At every moment energy corporations have made capital investment in the past, which interfere with alternative decisions in the present, since the invested capital has to be written off in the future. Therefore, it is an important task of politics to set the frame of reference in such a way, that this vicious circle can be broken. It is a wrong excuse to rely on market mechanisms, when the market is prevented from working, due to the highly concentrated economic (and political) power of large energy corporations.

Therefore it is necessary,

- Firstly to channel research funds from research on nuclear and fossil energy sources to alternative (solar) energy, to research on technical and social measures of increasing energy efficiency, and last but not least, to research on the many possibilities for an alternative and sustainable development model, that could avoid and save energy,

- Secondly, to subsidise over a limited period of time, alternative energy sources. This is justified since they produce social benefits, whereas nuclear energy is highly subsidised, although the social costs of the energy source are incalculably high.

- Thirdly, the IAEA shall be reshaped into an International Alternative Energy Association

      (1) promoting the proliferation of renewable solar energy and of technologies apt to increase energy efficiency,

      (2) helping to shut down all nuclear power plants in the world, in a period of time as short as possible and

      (3) developing a safe solution for the final disposal of already existing nuclear waste.

- Fourthly, the international community has to develop compensation mechanisms for all people concerned, especially for poor countries, in order to make them capable of following these rules.

6. The limits of "joint implementation"

Therefore the strategies of "joint implementation", recommended also on the Climate Summit in Berlin (1995), are only a transitory solution to the energy problem. Joint implementation on the one hand, can positively help reduce CO_2 emissions on a world-wide level, but on the other hand they negatively hinder technological innovations and technology transfer (because it is not the most developed technology introduced in power plants in Third World countries), and even worse, they prevent from switching from the fossil and nuclear energy model to that of alternative, renewable energies.

9. TOWARDS ANOTHER VISION OF HUMAN RIGHTS

Listening to the voices of the people of Chernobyl, it has become clearer that the concepts and categories, enshrined in the dominant human rights discourse, have become increasingly insufficient to grasp the violence of the times. While we need to extend the horizons, and deepen the existing human rights discourse, we need also a new generation of human rights.

We need to refuse the paradigm that has understood human rights as the rights of the powerful, the rights of the privileged. We need to listen to the voices of those who do not share that power. We need to listen to the voices of the victims of nuclear testing in the Pacific, of uranium miners in Namibia, the workers and communities of nuclear plants in India, in Sellafield, in Chelyabinsk, to the indigenous populations of the US, in Canada, the Aborigines in Australia, to the women who give birth to "jelly babies" in Micronesia and Polynesia, to the children of Chernobyl.

What does the fundamental right to life mean to the genetically damaged children born and to the millions yet unborn ?

The nuclear industry undermines the discourse of human justice. There are today at least 32 million nuclear victims, produced by the world's nuclear industries and weapons testing. They are the first victims of the third world war, waged by a nuclear industry, which in the name of national security, peace, safe energy, even sustainable development, victimises an increasing number of people. The nuclear establishments in all nation states, abrogate several fundamental freedoms (from the right to information, to the increasing surveillance of peace and anti-nuclear movements) enshrined in the UN charter, and in almost all national constitutions. Nation states, it would seem, have the right to destruction; and peoples and communities have no right to prevent or stop that destruction.

How does the International Covenant on Genocide translate into a world of nuclear technology ? For radiation obliterates whole peoples, whole civilisations. Chernobyl is about the destruction of a people. Is this not criminal? Are these not crimes against humanity ? For nuclear power plants, missile ranges and military bases have displaced entire populations, driving them to a desperate and denigrated existence. They are indeed refugees in their own country.

The dominant human rights discourse is locked into the individual nation state paradigm, blurring all stratification and communities in society. The liberal discourse on rights is focused on the rights of individuals against states. Individual rights and freedoms provided the essential tenants on which the edifice of human rights was built and developed, and for which the nation state was the guarantor. The United Nations Declaration on Human Rights and all the other covenants on human rights to which the nation state are signatories, clearly elucidate the rights that must be assured to the citizens of a state. The nation states are then given the responsibility for upholding these rights. However, the nation states may then legitimise the most brutal repression on its own people (concealing nuclear crimes for instance) which are then seen as the internal concern, the law and order, the national security of these sovereign nation states. The nation state, from guarantor of human rights, is often its greatest violator.

And as in the case of Chernobyl, where do the people take those responsible for redress of the violence done to them ? Where do they seek reparation, even compensation ?

There exists no mechanism at the international level, by which a sovereign people may take a sovereign nation state to task. In the International Court of Justice, nation states may seek redress and reparation from another nation state. But the victims of nation state policies, whether of war, or development or nuclear technology have no locus standi in the World Court. There is an urgent need to develop a new international mechanism/institution based on principles of obligations towards peoples, where peoples and communities who have been violated by the policies of nation states, may seek redress and compensation from them.

We need urgently a new jurisprudence on human rights, that would encapsulate in its vision the right of all peoples to be human; that would explore new terrain on liabilities across boundaries, on the extent of responsibility when nuclear radiation is involved, on compensation when long term and future violence is feared. We need to extend the horizons of human rights; to explore new paths beyond the parameters of existing human knowledge. We need to find new perspectives on the universality of human rights, while we seek possibilities to extend its parameters. We need also to explore a new discourse, in dialogue with the cultural perspectives of reality, finding other notions of development, of democracy, even dissent; other notions of equality, dignity and justice; other notions of rights that would recognise the rights of communities and the collective rights of peoples. In the existing human rights paradigms, the nation state is unable to address the rights of communities in the context of their needs. Perhaps in the understanding of the needs of individuals and communities, and not only being confined to the rights of individuals, can a way be found to transform the human rights discourse, may we then seek other visions of governance, because humankind proffers many horizons of discourse.

And because our eyes do not, as yet, behold these horizons, it does not mean that these horizons do not exist.

JUDGEMENT

The Tribunal condemns :

- The International Atomic Energy Agency (IAEA),
- the national commissions for atomic energy and
- the governments which support and finance them, on behalf of the interests of the nuclear industry :

* for trying to promote nuclear energy, through falsehood, intimidation, and unethical use of money power

* for their attempts to suppress all forms of alternative renewable and sustainable sources of energy

* for their violation of the most fundamental rights of the victims of nuclear accidents, including their revictimisation, and the arrogant denial of their suffering

* for the perseverance of an arrogant attitude of denial of people's suffering, right up to the closing session of the IAEA's last meeting in Vienna, on 12 April 1996

- The International Commission for Radiation Protection (ICRP), whose policy is clearly inspired by the promotion of the nuclear industry, instead of being aimed at the protection of the potential victims.

The Tribunal blames :

Those in the scientific community who do not stand up, to safeguard the honour of their profession, in the face of pressure from the nucleocrats, and maintain a deafening silence, in spite of strong scientific evidence, regarding the omnicidal nature of the nuclear enterprise.

RECOMMENDATIONS AND PROPOSALS:

The mission of the Tribunal is to give a voice to the victims, in defence of their human rights.

The statement by the IAEA (International Atomic Energy Agency) Conference in Vienna, 8-12 April 1996, that the catastrophe of Chernobyl has caused 32 deaths, is an offence to the thousands of victims, and scandalises the informed public as well as the scientific community of the world. It is another of the numerous attempts of IAEA to deny and conceal the real radiation injuries and damages around Chernobyl, in order to continue to develop and spread nuclear installations, all over the world.

With respect to the human rights of the victims, the Tribunal recommends :

* that the current proposals to relax radiation protection standards for contaminated land and food, to relocate people on contaminated land and to return contaminated soils to agricultural uses, be immediately stopped.

* that the plight of the victims be made known world-wide, and the appeals for medical, economic and social assistance for the affected countries and individuals be assessed, and reported, by independent medical personnel. The technical staff of the IAEA, which is mandated with the promotion of nuclear energy, cannot be considered competent to this purpose.

* the immediate reduction of permissible radiation-exposure levels, both for workers and for the general public, bringing the radiation standards, at least with respect to fatal cancers causation, more in line with standard practice, exercised in toxicology and occupational health for chemical pollutants.

The Tribunal has arrived to the unanimous conclusion, that the promotion and the proliferation of nuclear technology cannot be sustained, and that one of the main reasons for inadequate safeguarding of fission material is IAEA's and all national Atomic Energy Commissions incompatibility of promotion and control. Control is executed in a half-hearted manner, as promotion is the priority. Nuclear material and dangerous installations however, require much more stringent control measures than those currently practised.

Therefore,

* Nuclear industry has to be banned for civilian as well as for military use

* The current mandate for the IAEA to promote this technology be withdrawn by the UN, and a new mandate be drawn up to assure:

    - responsible operation and systemic shut down of currently operating reactors
    - the monitoring of radioactive wastes
    - the safe dismantling of shut down reactors
    - the rigorous control of fissile material
    - the compensation of the victims of nuclear industry
    - the restoration of radioactive environmental damages.

The Tribunal envisions decentralised and alternative energy sources, which respect human needs and limitations, which do not cause fear, and which are better scaled to endpoint uses, in a democratic decentralised society.

For this reason it recommends :

* reshaping of the IAEA into an International Alternative Energy Association to deal with putting forward sustainable energies

* implementation of the Rio Agenda 21 resolution to set an International Court of the Environment, where issues involving transboundary pollution can be addressed

* experimentation with models of democratic functioning above the level of national states and the current limits which the nations place on participation in decision making, including that of NGO's

* deliberate strategies to include a feminine analysis and perspective into health and safety, and of effectively including concern for the rights of future generations, to a supporting environment and intact gene pool

* the proposed design of the International Court of the Environment, which recognises the rights of NGO's and individuals, to bring suits against polluters.

The Permanent People's Tribunal
listened to the people of Chernobyl
they spoke of a great violence
they came from a great silence
a silence that has begun to speak

they spoke in a language of suffering
refusing that Chernobyl becomes
one more forgotten narrative of our times
refusing that their tears dry

they spoke in a language of knowledge
challenging the world not to accept
that the situation was "normal"
that nuclear energy was "safe"
that people could return

Chernobyl was about the uprooting of
communities
about the destruction of a people
Chernobyl was about miracles that have
somehow survived
Chernobyl was that the worst is yet to come.

CHERNOBYL
CHILDREN'S PROJECT

Anatol Kljashchuk

In Belarus, a small country between Russia and Poland, over a million children are at risk of developing cancer because of a nuclear accident which happened almost ten years ago.

Holidays abroad can boost the children's immune systems and increase their resistance to serious disease. Vitamins, drugs and medical equipment are desperately needed by Belarussian hospitals and orphanages.

The Chernobyl Children's Project was launched in Ireland six years ago and has brought more than 2,000 children for recuperative holidays and sent hundreds of tons of aid to the victims of the world's worst nuclear disaster.

A branch of the Project, established in Manchester in January 1995, brought 38 children to the High Peak and the Lancashire countryside during its first Summer; and has sent six ambulances and forty tons of medical aid to Belarus. Manchester is now the co-ordination centre for Chernobyl Children's Project (UK) which has more than a dozen branches around the country, and brought 150 children to Britain in the Summer of 1996.

☐ *I would like more information about the Chernobyl Children's Project*

☐ *I enclose a donation of £ ....*

Name: ....

Address: ....

....

....

....

Postcode: ....

Telephone: ....

On behalf of the children of Belarus we would like to thank you for your interest and for any help you are able to give.

CHERNOBYL
CHILDREN'S PROJECT

One World Centre, 6 Mount Street, Manchester, M2 5NS.

Yorkshire Bank, Manchester
Sort Code 05-05-73 A/c No.68145433

Chernobyl Children's Project is a company limited by guarantee. Registration No. 3220045. Charitable status is now being sought. September 1996

How *You* Can Help the Children of Chernobyl

£2.50
will provide a child with vitamins for 6 months.

£5
will provide life-saving medicine for one year for a child whose thyroid gland has been removed.

£25
will provide the painkillers for a child with terminal cancer to die with dignity.

£200
will provide an airfare for a holiday which will boost a child's immune system.

CHERNOBYL
CHILDREN'S PROJECT

ПОДДЕРЖКА ДЕТЯМ
БЕЛАРУСИ

One World Centre, 6 Mount Street, Manchester M2 5NS. Tel: 0161 834 8176 Fax: 0161 834 8187

WE'VE EXPERIMENTED
ON OUR OWN PEOPLE

Nuclear weapons drove us to the unspeakable act of secretly testing radiation on our own population. 23,000 American civilians were subjected to radiation research in about 1,400 projects over thirty years. The government tested on retarded children, mental patients, poor women, and US soldiers. More than 200,000 troops were ordered to observe nuclear test detonations and were exposed to radiation.

WE'VE ABUSED
INDIGENOUS PEOPLE

Every nuclear test site in the world is on indigenous land. New nuclear waste sites, loaded with financial incentives, are constantly planned for native land. Right now, 40,000 tons are destined for the Mescalero Apache reservation in New Mexico.

In less than a life time the waste from nuclear weapons, power plants and the nuclear industry has permeated nearly every sector of the globe--silently undermining the health and life expectancy of humankind and other species. Many of these nuclear poisons will remain potent for as long as 250,000 years.

WORST OF ALL--WE'RE
STILL DOING IT

We are spending $33 billion annually to maintain our nuclear forces of which $3.3 billion is budgeted for nuclear weapons, underground, and virtual reality computer equipment that will enable our Dr. Strangeloves to develop nukes in space and other exotic lethal weapons.

LETHAL RADIATION CONTINUES
TO POISON OUR WORKERS
& COMMUNITIES

While the nuclear industry thrives, workers who handle and transport these radioactive materials and wastes risk exposure.

New Mexico

*Retrospective studies of mostly Native American uranium miners show heart disease deaths eleven times that of normal (unexposed) populations and a lung cancer rate forty times above the normal expected incidence. (1)

WOMEN'S NUCLEAR
FREE NETWORK

c/o Feminists for a Compassionate Society
PO Box 868, Kyle TX 78640, USA
Tel: (512) 262-2300 FAX (512)268-1471

Produced by Yana Bland Ph.D.
of the Feminists for a Compassionate Society
Pamela Ransom of the Women's Environment and
Development Organization (WEDO)
Alice Slater of Global Resource Action Center for the
Environment (GRACE)

PARTICIPATING ORGANIZATIONS

Feminists for a Compassionate Society
Women's Environment and
Development Organization (WEDO)
Global Resource Action Center for the Environment (GRACE)
Grandmothers for Peace International
The Livermore Conversion Project
The Peace Farm
Association of Women of the Mediterranean Region
National Environmental Coalition of Native Americans (NECONA)
Concerned Mothers & Women of Three Mile Island
Nuclear Guardianship Project
Plutonium Free Future Women's Network
Río Grande/Río Bravo

WE'VE WASTED PRECIOUS
RESOURCES---$4,000,000,000,000

Four trillion dollars - that's what the US has spent on
Nuclear Weapons over the past fifty years.

WE'VE POLLUTED OUR
OWN ENVIRONMENT

We've created more than 4,500 contaminated sites,
covering tens of thousands of acres which may take 75
years and cost as high as one trillion dollars to "clean
up". "Clean-up" of toxic plutonium, which remains
lethal for over 250,000 years, is the wrong word. At
best, we can only attempt to manage and contain the
poisons from seeping into the air and groundwater and
visiting further destruction on our people.

PUBLICATIONS LIST

From Saigon to Sarajevo:Mass Media in Times of War

Journalists, including active war correspondents, and scientists look at the role of the press, TV and radio in periods of armed conflict. Issues covered include: the Gulf War, Afghanistan, Bosnia-Herzegovina, and racism in reporting. Contributors include Phillip Knightley, Julius Fortuna, Gloria Emerson and Sören Sommelius. 100pp. Retail 15 CHF, libraries/institutions 20 CHF.

The Unfinished Disarmament Agenda

Comprehensive survey of the whole field of disarmament: weapons of mass destruction, conventional and inhumane weapons, verification, relationship to development, conflicts, environment, culture, role of NGOs and the UN. Edited by the Special NGO Committee for Disarmament, Geneva. 70 pp, published by the United Nations, 1995. NOW AVAILABLE FREE.

The Right to Refuse Military Orders

Examines the application of the Nuremberg Principles to situations of war and oppression, including Vietnam, Romania, and the Occupied Territories. Issues raised include resistance to nuclear weapons, military service, torture and repression of strikers. Soldiers, lawyers and activists all contribute valuable perspectives. Available also in Finnish. Ed. Merja Pentikäinen, 112pp. Retail: 10 CHF, 15 for institutions/libraries.

From Hiroshima to the Hague

Comprehensive guide to the World Court Project on the legal status of nuclear weapons. Keith Mothersson, Institute for Law & Peace, UK. 187pp, 1992. Retail 15 CHF, libraries 20 CHF.

100 Years of Peacemaking

Indispensable history of the IPB and other peace movement organisations and networks. Rainer Santi, former IPB Secretary-General. Also available in Swedish, Finnish, German. 100pp, 1991. Retail 10 CHF, Libraries/institutions 15 CHF.

IPB Centenary Exhibition Catalogue

Illustrated survey of peace movement achievements. Published in association with the UN's League of Nations Archives. 35pp, 1992. Retail 10 CHF.

Tackling the Flow of Arms

An international survey of campaigns and initiatives against the arms trade. Ernst Gülcher, International Peace Information Service, Antwerp. 179 pp, 1992. Retail 15CHF, libraries/institutions 20 CHF.

Youth and Conscription

Includes history of objection to military service, impact on women, and case studies. Kimmo Kiljunen and Juoko Väänänen. Published with War Resisters International and Peace Union of Finland. 272 pp, 1987- Retail 5CHF.

IPB News is published quarterly and mailed free to members. It can also be purchased separately from the secretariat for 5 CHF, including postage, per copy. A 12-month subscription costs 20 CHF (individs) or 50 CHF (institutions).

TO ORDER:

Contact Secretariat. All orders must be prepaid. Orders will be sent by book post (surface rate) upon receipt of payment. Discount rates for IPB members, bulk sales, and low-income countries - contact us for details.

How to transfer money to IPB

Our 1st choices (no charges for IPB):
- in Swiss Francs (CHF) direct to our Geneva Post Office Giro account (CCP. 12-2014-6).
- in Norway, transfer to Postgiro account: 0824 0564611.
- in Swiss Francs by bank transfer to our main bank account (Banque Coop., Geneva, No.140049.290090-9); or by cheque in £ sterling sent to our Geneva office.

Alternatively:
- by cheque in US dollars OR Swiss francs, sent to our Geneva office. N.B. For a $ cheque we have to pay up to $8 just to cash it.
- cash in any major currency (this saves us bank charges but could be risky if sent by standard mail).
- International Postal Reply Coupons - for small amounts.

Whichever method you choose, please indicate 'fees 95', 'literature', 'donation' etc and sender's name and address.
Note: All donations are tax-deductible; IPB is a non-profit association registered under Swiss law.

To the:
Low Level Radiation Campaign,
9 North Road,
Builth Wells,
Powys LD2 3BU
UK. (☎01982 552502 or 0378 254588
e-mail: cato@gn.apc.org)

Please send me your
16 page Campaign action guide ☐

I want to subscribe to the Campaign
newsletter *Radioactive Times*
(Subscription for 4 issues per ☐
year £6.00/ £12.00 groups)

Please send me ......copies of *Wings of
Death*
by Chris Busby @ £10.99 ☐

Please send me .... packs of this ☐
leaflet, with a display unit

I want to support the work of the
Campaign and enclose a donation ☐ £
of

Total enclosed .... ☐ £
Please make cheques payable to
"Low Level Radiation Campaign"
[Bank Code 40 1514 account 21058614]

Name ....

Address..

....

..................................Postcode..............

☎ ....

INTERNATIONAL PERSPECTIVES

IN

PUBLIC

HEALTH

Editor-in-Chief
Rosalie Bertell, Ph.D., G.N.S.H.

Associate Editors:

Rajender Chawla, Ph.D.
Kentucky, U.S.A.

Gerald Drake, M.D.
Michigan, U.S.A.

Bernd Franke, M.Sc.
Heidelberg, F.R.G.

Michio Kaku, Ph.D.
New York, U.S.A.

David Kattenburg, Ph.D.
Nicaragua

Marie Claire Kennedy,
Ph.D., S.S.J.
Pennsylvania, U.S.A.

Karl Z. Morgan, Ph.D.
Georgia, U.S.A.

G.M. Oza, Ph.D.
Baroda, India

Beverly Paigen, Ph.D.
Maine, U.S.A.

H.M. Pandit, Ph.D.
New York, U.S.A.

Daniel Pisello, Ph.D.
New York, U.S.A.

Jean Rossel, Ph.D.
Newchatel, Switzerland

Avery Sandberg, M.D.
Arizona, U.S.A.

Gladys Schmitz, R.N., S.S.N.D.
Illinois, U.S.A.

Inge Schmitz-Feuerhake, Ph.D.
Bremen, F.R.G.

T.P. Speed, Ph.D.
Nedlands, Australia

David Spence, M.D., M.P.H.
Alaska, U.S.A.

Address correspondence to:
Ministry of Concern for Public Health
PO Box 1487
Buffalo NY 14231-1487 USA

Send Manuscripts to:
International Institute of Concern for Public Health
710–264 Queens Quay West
Toronto ON M5J 1B5 Canada

Subscriptions:
Subscription for four issues:
$25.00 U.S. for delivery in the U.S. and Canada
$30.00 U.S. for overseas delivery
Checks or money orders should be in U.S.$, payable to Ministry of Concern for
Public Health.